AGS

ECONOMICS

by
Carol Sullivan, B.S.
and
Jane Wilcox Smith, M.A.

AGS®

American Guidance Service, Inc.
4201 Woodland Road
Circle Pines, MN 55014-1796
1-800-328-2560

Images:
Cover, background flag photo, PhotoDisc; p. 11, PhotoDisc; p. 27, all, PhotoDisc; p.36, Tony Stone Images; p. 46, Corbis; p. 62, PhotoDisc; p. 78, PhotoDisc.

Printed in the United States of America

ISBN 0-7854-2420-2

Order Number: 91545

A 0 9 8 7 6 5 4 5 3

Contents

The Meaning of Economics

Economics is the study of how people's **needs** and **wants** are taken care of by their own efforts to earn a living. It is also the study of how countries use **resources** to provide **goods and services.** Resources are all the things that **producers** use to make goods and to provide services. These goods and services are used to take care of the wishes of their citizens. For example, petroleum is used to provide heat for people's homes or energy for their automobiles.

Americans Live in a Free Enterprise System

Every living person, no matter how old or young, is affected by some economic system. Individuals are an important part of the American **free enterprise system.** In this system, the individual can make many choices, whether deciding what to buy or what type of job to look for.

The study of economics and the American free enterprise system involves many things that are a part of daily life. These things include **money** (something accepted as payment), jobs, things people want, and things people need in order to live. People worry about having what they need. People need food to eat, a safe and comfortable place to live, someone to care for them if they become ill, and enough money to provide them with all these things. There are not enough goods for all people to have everything they may dream about. However, individuals can get the things they want by carefully planning their spending. People can work extra hours or seek better jobs to earn the money to buy what they want.

Needs and Wants

Studying economics helps build an understanding of how goods and services are produced in the United States. People's needs and wants are taken care of by goods and services. People need **material goods** such as food and clothing. Yet services such as police protection and education are also necessary for a high quality of life.

People Are Important in a Free Enterprise System

Individuals are **consumers.** This means they use goods and services. People are one of the most important parts of the free enterprise system. Producers need to sell their goods and services to be successful. A **labor force** or workforce is necessary for businesses to work. People who own and operate businesses are known as **entrepreneurs.**

Money Is an Important Part of Economics

Money is anything people accept as payment. For example, money is used to buy bread from a bakery. The bakery in turn uses the money to buy wheat and other supplies to make the bread. The American free enterprise system has worked well. Citizens of the United States enjoy a high **standard of living,** which can be described as a good and comfortable life. This means most citizens, not all, have the money to pay for the things that make their lives comfortable.

In a free enterprise system, consumers can choose what to buy.

A. Circle the correct answer in each of the following sentences.

1. (Resources, Economics) is the study of how people's needs and wants are taken care of.

2. Economics is the study of how a country uses its (resources, products) to provide goods and services for its people.

3. In (a free enterprise system, all economic systems), people can choose where to work or what to buy.

4. A (consumer, producer) makes goods or services for people to use.

5. A (consumer, producer) uses the goods and services made in a country.

6. People may be part of a (consumer, labor) force, which is necessary for businesses to work.

7. (Entrepreneurs, Workers) own and operate their own businesses.

8. Most Americans enjoy a (high, low) standard of living because of their free enterprise system.

B. Make a list of five of your needs and wants. Remember, needs are things that people must have to live.

Needs   Wants

1. _____   1. _____

2. _____   2. _____

3. _____   3. _____

4. _____   4. _____

5. _____   5. _____

C. Choose boldface words from the lesson to complete each of the following sentences. Write the words in the puzzle below.

1. Economics teaches how _____ are used to provide goods and services.

2. Police protection and education are _____ of an economic system.

3. Material _____ are such things as food and clothing.

4. A person owning and operating a business is an _____ .

5. A comfortable life for most citizens may be called a high _____ .

6. _____ is anything people accept as payment.

7. In a free _____ system, an individual has many choices.

8. A _____ uses the goods and services of an economic system.

9. Citizens' _____ and wants are taken care of by goods and services.

1. __ e __ __ __ __ __ __ __
2. __ __ __ __ __ c __ __
3. __ o __ __ __
4. __ __ __ __ __ __ __ __ n __ __ __
5. __ __ __ __ __ __ __ __ o __ __ __ __ __ __ __
6. m __ __ __ __
7. __ __ __ __ __ __ __ i __ __
8. c __ __ __ __ __ __ __
9. __ __ __ __ s

The Development of Economics

Early Economic Systems Were Simple

Economic systems began developing thousands of years ago. When human beings lived in tribal groups, they depended on nature for food, clothing, and shelter. Men hunted and fished. Women and children gathered nuts and berries. Animal skins provided clothing. Caves were used for shelter. In early times, human needs were simple and were satisfied by nature.

Slowly, this simple economic system changed. **Agriculture**, or farming, developed as humans learned to grow and to store food. This allowed groups to remain in one place rather than having to wander in search of the things they needed. This change in lifestyle meant that there was time for new things, such as making tools and pottery and creating art and music. These farming groups slowly developed into villages, and then into towns and cities. In time, they traded with each other. However, as the economic conditions of these groups improved, other problems developed. A major difficulty was group protection.

Feudalism Became Popular in Many Countries of Europe

Wars between villages meant that some people were taken over by others. To avoid becoming slaves of other groups, villagers sought protection in a system known as **feudalism.** Feudalism was a system in which a feudal lord gave protection to the people who lived and worked for him on his land, or **fief.** In return, the people, who were called **serfs,** gave loyalty and economic support to the feudal lord. In this important economic system, different duties were divided among the people. Some were farmers, some were weapons makers, and some were soldiers. The feudal lords were powerful. When a lord died, the lord's son received the lord's land and control of the serfs who worked the land. This system of feudalism survived in Europe for many centuries.

Agriculture developed as humans learned to grow and store food.

A. The facts below are not in the correct order in which they took place in the development of economics. Write a 1 in front of the first thing that happened, a 2 in front of the second thing, and so on.

_____ **A.** Villages, towns, and cities traded with each other.

_____ **B.** Tribal groups depended on nature for food, clothes, and shelter.

_____ **C.** Humans learned to grow and to store food.

_____ **D.** Under feudalism, a lord protected his people.

Guilds Developed in Cities and Towns

The power of feudalism weakened as people began to leave the rural areas and go to the towns and cities. The economic systems of towns and cities depended on trade. Trade caused an increase in production. Trade with Asia (which brought such things as silks and spices) caused the towns and cities to grow. As they grew, the **guild** economic system developed. A guild is a group of workers with similar interests.

Two types of guilds developed. The first kind was a **merchant's guild.** It regulated weights and measures as well as the types and **prices** of goods to be sold. Price is the amount of money a consumer must pay for a good or service. As the production of goods became more varied, the **craft guild** developed. There was a craft guild for each separate group of skilled workers, such as carpenters or tailors. The function of the craft guilds included training others in the trade and overseeing individual shops.

Two systems developed later. When workers produced goods in their homes, the system was called the **domestic system.** The system in which goods were produced in owned or rented buildings, called factories, was known as the **factory system.**

Mercantilism Replaced the Factory System

As the number of factories grew, a new system known as **mercantilism** developed. Mercantilism was a system based on the idea that a country would become strong if it stored up a great deal of wealth. Under this system, the government took strict control of the collection of **taxes** (money that people and businesses pay to the government) and the making of goods. In addition, the government made certain that the number of products sold to foreign countries was greater than the number of foreign products bought. The government was also interested in having a population large enough to supply needed workers and soldiers.

American Colonists Favored the Free Enterprise System

Free enterprise developed in the American colonies as a result of the effects of British mercantilism. England weakened the colonial economic system by pressuring the colonists to send raw materials to Europe. The colonies were also pressured to buy English goods. This system forced the colonies into debt, but made England rich.

After the American Revolution brought independence to the colonies, the free enterprise system replaced mercantilism. In a free enterprise system, the individual, not the government, controls economic power. Each person has the right to make his or her own choices about economic matters.

Adam Smith: Father of Modern Economics

In 1776, a Scottish economist named Adam Smith wrote *An Inquiry Into the Nature and Causes of the Wealth of Nations.* In this book, he put forth his ideas about a new kind of economic system in which business would operate without government control. He said that individual self-interest, private ownership, and competing businesses would help an economic system to succeed. Smith said freedom of choice, both for the individual and for business, was all that was needed to make a country strong.

Adam Smith

His ideas appealed to the colonists. People followed his suggestions. Most colonists had left England because they were denied individual freedom. The free enterprise system Smith described worked for the colonists in America, and it continues to work for Americans today.

B. Circle the correct answer in each of the following sentences.

1. A (craft, merchant's) guild regulated the type of goods to be sold.

2. When goods were made in rented or owned buildings, a (domestic, factory) system developed.

3. One function of a (merchant's, craft) guild was to train others in a trade.

4. In a system of (free enterprise, mercantilism), a country tried to grow wealthy by strict government control.

5. In a system of (free enterprise, mercantilism), the individual has the right to make choices.

Resources Are Used to Produce Goods and Services   Lesson 3

What are Resources?

Resources are all the materials that producers use to make goods and to provide services. The materials and the people used to do the work are resources needed by businesses. This work that people do for businesses can be either **physical** (doing) or **mental** (thinking). In an automobile plant, for example, the cars are designed by thinkers and built by doers. This mixture of material resources and human resources is necessary to make the American economic system work well.

Physical labor is supplied by human resources.

A. Choose words from the paragraph about resources to complete each of the following sentences. Write the words in the spaces provided.

1. _____ are needed to make goods and to provide services.

2. The work that people do for businesses can be either _____ or physical.

3. The American economic system uses a mixture of two kinds of resources:

    _____ and

    _____ .

Three Classes of Resources

The resources needed in the production of goods and services are grouped into three classes.

The term **natural resources** means all the things in nature that are needed to produce goods and services. Forests, oil, water, and farm fields are examples of natural resources. The United States has a large supply of natural resources, such as water, trees, and good farm soil. Some resources, however, must be bought from other countries. For example, the United States imports oil, certain minerals, and natural rubber.

Although the United States has a good supply of resources in the world, it is still possible to use up resources if people are not careful. Trees must be replanted. Water can become **polluted,** or dirty, in many areas. Once this happens to water, it is difficult to make it pure again. Coal and oil cannot be easily replaced. It takes thousands of years for nature to produce coal and oil.

B. Choose words from the paragraphs on page 11 to complete these sentences. Write the words in the spaces provided.

1. Natural resources are all the things found in _____ that are needed to produce goods and services.

2. Three examples of natural resources that are plentiful in the United States are
   a. _____ b. _____ c. _____

3. Coal and _____ cannot be easily replaced.

THREE TYPES OF RESOURCES

Land	Labor	Capital

  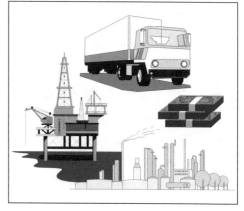

Labor is another valuable resource. Labor is the work humans do. People's skills are needed in the production of goods and services. Many American workers are highly skilled. They are encouraged to improve their skills because highly skilled workers receive higher **salaries,** or pay. Job training and education are available to people who want to improve their skills. Recently, machines have taken over some jobs that used to be done by unskilled workers. The use of machines has forced people to learn different skills. The labor needs of the producers of goods and services in America are always changing.

C. Choose words from the paragraph to complete each sentence.

1. _____ is the work humans do.

2. Higher _____ are paid to highly skilled workers.

3. Some jobs that were once done by unskilled workers are now done by _____ .

American Labor Force Percentages, 1999

Occupational Group (age 16 or older)	Percent of the Labor Force
Managerial and professional specialty	30
Technical, sales, and administrative support	29
Operators, fabricators, and laborers	14
Service occupations	13
Precision production, craft, and repair	11
Farming, forestry, and fishing	3

Source: Bureau of Labor Statistics

D. Study the chart above. Then complete the exercise.

1. What age group is represented in the chart? _____

2. What group makes up most of the labor force? _____

3. What group makes up the smallest part of the labor force? _____

4. What kind of work do you think people do who have a service occupation?

   _____

5. How much larger is the technical, sales, and administrative support group than the service occupations group? _____

6. Which group makes up 11 percent of the labor force? _____

7. Which group makes up 30 percent of the labor force? _____

8. Combined, how much of the labor force do the managerial and professional specialty group and the technical, sales, and administrative support group represent?

   _____

9. What kind of work do you think people do who have a technical job?

   _____

10. In what occupational group would a forest ranger be placed?

    _____

11. In what occupational group would someone who fixes cars be placed?

    _____

12. In what kind of work setting would most people in the managerial and professional specialty group work? _____

E. Study the chart below. Then answer the questions.

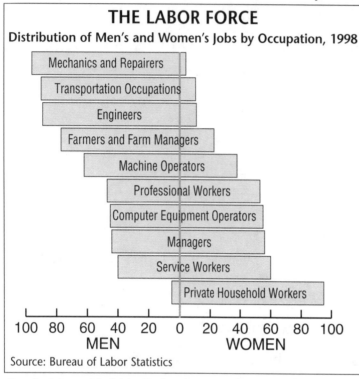

THE LABOR FORCE
Distribution of Men's and Women's Jobs by Occupation, 1998

Mechanics and Repairers
Transportation Occupations
Engineers
Farmers and Farm Managers
Machine Operators
Professional Workers
Computer Equipment Operators
Managers
Service Workers
Private Household Workers

100 80 60 40 20 0 20 40 60 80 100
MEN   WOMEN

Source: Bureau of Labor Statistics

1. What five occupations have more women than men? _____ _____ _____

2. How many occupations have more men than women? _____

3. What three occupations have less than 15 percent women? _____ _____

4. What occupation has less than 15 percent men? _____

5. What occupation has about 40 percent women? _____

Capital is a third kind of resource. Capital refers to the actual items that are needed for production. Tools, machinery, and factories are capital. The trucks and highways that are needed to send goods from place to place are capital. Buildings, docks, and anything else a business needs for production are capital. Money is also thought of as capital. It is needed to pay for all the things mentioned above. The United States has the money to supply most of the capital goods needed to produce goods and services.

F. Write *Land, Labor,* or *Capital* after each resource listed below.

1. tractor _____

2. police officer _____

3. water _____

4. doctor _____

5. engineer _____

6. forest _____

7. crude oil _____

8. computer _____

9. cornfield _____

10. factory _____

11. shipyard _____

12. rubber _____

13. highway _____

14. carpenter _____

15. marble _____

Three Basic Questions

In the definition of economics in Lesson 1, you read that countries have to decide how best to use the resources they have. How will natural resources, human workers, factories, and farm fields be used? Most of the resources that a country has are **scarce**. Scarce means that there is not enough of these resources to satisfy all the wants of all the people. People's wants are endless. A country must ask three questions about the use of its natural resources.

What Shall Be Produced?

The basic needs of people must be taken care of first: food, clothing, and shelter. People living in different areas have different basic needs. Americans in the South have different eating habits from those in the North. Most Americans have the money to buy more than basic needs. They have extra money to spend on **luxuries**, expensive items that are not necessary for life, such as cars, stereos, vacations, and jewelry. American producers must keep this fact in mind when deciding what to produce.

Other important questions must also be considered about the well-being and safety of citizens. Should a country spend its money and resources to make more weapons for defense or more consumer goods? Should land be used for public parks and recreation or for more office buildings?

How Shall Goods and Services Be Produced?

After deciding what to produce, a country must look at its resources. Then it must decide the best way to produce

SCARCITY
The Fundamental Economic Problem

Seemingly Unlimited Wants

Limited Resources

SCARCITY

CHOICES

| WHAT To Produce | HOW To Produce | FOR WHOM To Produce |

Scarcity is the fundamental economic problem which forces people to use resources wisely.

such items as electricity, steel, machinery, and consumer goods. Modern inventions make it possible for much human labor to be done by machines. In some countries, it is still cheaper to use human labor. In the United States, however, it is cheaper and better for machines to replace unskilled human labor. America has more skilled workers than unskilled workers.

For Whom Shall the Goods and Services Be Produced?

How will the goods and services be given out to consumers? Consumers must buy the goods and services produced. The amount of an individual's **income,** or money earned, will decide how much can be bought. In the American free enterprise system, most people can buy the basic things they need for survival plus much more. In some cases, even basic needs cannot be bought because a person's or family's income is too low. The government must help these people by supplying their basic needs.

All Economic Systems Must Answer the Three Basic Questions

The questions just discussed are the same for all economic systems. The differences are seen in the way the questions are answered. In a free enterprise system as in the United States, there are many ways to answer these questions. Producers must be aware of what consumers will buy. The country can use its resources to make sure its citizens are safe and well.

A. **Complete the answers to each of the following statements.**

1. The _____ of most people are endless.

2. Most of the _____ that a country has are scarce.

3. List three examples of basic needs. _____

_____

4. List three examples of luxuries. _____

_____

5. Modern _____ have made it possible for much human labor to be replaced by machines.

B. **Match the terms on the left with the definitions on the right. Write the correct letter on the line before each term.**

_____ 1. resources   a. extra money may be spent on these

_____ 2. clothing   b. can replace unskilled human labor

_____ 3. weapons for defense   c. needed to produce goods

_____ 4. income   d. money earned

_____ 5. scarce   e. a basic human need

_____ 6. machines   f. a country may choose to make these

_____ 7. needs   g. not enough of something

_____ 8. luxuries   h. people should satisfy these first

_____ 9. government   i. helps some people with low income

_____ 10. consumers   j. buy the goods and services that are produced

Review Unit 1

A. Match each term in the first column with the correct definition in the second column.

_____ 1. economics

_____ 2. capital

_____ 3. labor

_____ 4. natural resources

_____ 5. feudalism

_____ 6. mercantilism

_____ 7. scarce

_____ 8. free enterprise

a. includes factories, trucks, tools, and the money to buy these things

b. means that there is a limited supply

c. gives people many free choices

d. can be physical or mental

e. is an economic system where a feudal lord is in charge of the people

f. are things found in nature and used in production

g. means strong government control of economic matters

h. is a study of how goods and services are produced

B. Complete the exercise below. Write the correct questions on the lines provided.

1. Each economic system must ask this question when considering how the goods and services will be given out to consumers: _____

_____

2. When deciding whether to use machine or human labor, this question is asked:

_____

_____

3. When producers decide on the type of products to make to satisfy needs of consumers, they are answering this question: _____

_____

C. Write three examples for each class of resources below.

1. land: _____

2. labor: _____

3. capital: _____

Supply and Demand in the Market

Types of Markets

There are thousands of businesses in the United States. They provide goods and services for people. These goods and services must be bought and sold. A **market** is anywhere buying and selling take place. The market may be a small hardware store in a small neighborhood or a large department store in the city. A larger market may have buyers and sellers from different countries. In this international market, people may do business over the telephone and may never actually see each other. For instance, a buyer of fine diamonds may be in touch with sellers all over the world.

Another kind of market is the **stock market.** Here buyers and sellers have other people do their trading for them. Specially trained people buy and sell shares in businesses. These shares are called **stocks.** Until recently, these specially trained people were the only ones who bought and sold stock in this way. Now, because of advancements in computers, trading of socks can be done by anyone. Anyone with access to a computer and the Internet can trade in the stock market. Many people now buy and sell stocks on the Internet.

TYPES OF MARKETS		
Local Market	**International Market**	**Stock Market**
Buyers and sellers are in direct contact. Example: A large grocery or department store.	Buyers and sellers depend upon modern communication to contact each other. Example: Use of computer or telephone to sell oil or diamonds.	Buyers and sellers have someone else do their trading for them, or they trade for themselves using the Internet. Example: The New York Stock Exchange.

Markets Have Grown Larger

Modern inventions have caused markets to grow by making more goods available to the consumer. Air transportation moves goods rapidly to distant places. Refrigeration and freezing methods make it possible for foods that can spoil to be sent long distances. Hawaiian pineapples can be flown to the European market for sale. Australian beef can be bought and consumed by Americans. Telephone, computer, and telegraph communication make it possible for this buying and selling to be done easily.

Markets Control the Prices That Are Charged

How do sellers know what prices to ask for the products they sell? In the market, prices are set by **trial and error.** If sellers charge prices that are too high, no one will buy their products. If this happens, prices will then have to be lowered. Sometimes buyers want to buy products at very low prices, but none may be offered at that price. Then a buyer must either pay the price that the seller is charging or do without the product.

Small Markets Work the Same as Large Markets

Have you ever tried something that did not work? You may have had to keep on trying until you found something that worked. You used a trial and error method to do this. The young man in the following story also used trial and error.

Trial and Error: Selling a Bicycle

John wants to sell his bicycle. He wants the money to help pay for a new, more expensive racing bike. In a newspaper advertisement, he offers to sell the bike for $75. However, no one wishes to pay the price after learning the type of bike for sale. Someone offers $25, but John cannot let it go too low if he wants to buy a new racing bike. Finally, John lowers the price from $75 to $50. Three of his friends offer to buy it. He tells them that he will take the best offer, and he quickly sells the bike to one of them for $54. This is not as much as John had hoped for, but he can still hope to buy his racing bike if he continues to save for it. Through trial and error, John set a price that satisfied his needs as a seller. He also pleased the consumer, or buyer, who purchased the bicycle.

A. Read the phrases below. Write the phrase that will correctly complete each sentence on the line.

• the stock market	• fine diamonds
• will buy the product or service	• any place where buying and selling is done
• because of modern inventions	• supermarkets or department stores
• a trial and error system	

1. A market is _____ .

2. Markets have grown larger _____ .

3. An international market might buy and sell _____ .

4. Specially trained people buy and sell shares in _____ .

5. Two examples of local markets are _____ .

6. If prices are too high, no one _____ .

7. John tried to sell his bicycle by using _____ .

What Are Supply and Demand?

Supply is the amount of a product that is offered for sale. **Demand** is the amount of a product that consumers want to buy. In economics, we have the following laws:

- Law of Supply—Businesses will produce more goods at higher prices than they will produce at lower prices.

- Law of Demand—People will buy more goods at lower prices than they will buy at higher prices.

Supply and Demand Are Controlled by Consumers

After producers decide what to produce, they must decide on how much of a product or service to supply for consumers. Usually, the question of supply is decided by the consumer demand for a good or service. Many people may demand a certain style of automobile or jeans. There may not be enough of these popular items, so sellers are able to charge high prices for them. Consumers will pay high prices for popular products. Producers will then make more of these products. New producers may also begin supplying this product because of the high prices that can be charged and the high consumer demand. When production is increased in this manner, the supply will catch up to the demand, and prices will be lowered. For this reason, consumer demand for products can be said to control the supply of these products.

B. Choose the correct word to complete each sentence. Write each word on the line.

1. _____ demand can be said to control supply and demand. (Consumer, Producer)

2. High prices will cause more products to be _____ . (supplied, demanded)

3. _____ is the amount of a product that consumers want to buy. (Supply, Demand)

4. In the market, _____ are set by a trial and error system. (prices, products)

5. The law of supply states that businesses produce more goods at _____ prices. (higher, lower)

6. The law of demand states that people buy more goods at _____ prices. (higher, lower)

7. _____ is the amount of a product offered for sale. (Supply, Demand)

8. Consumers _____ pay high prices for popular products. (will, will not)

Prices Are Set in the Market

What Is a Market Price?

The **market price** is a price that most consumers will pay for a good or service. Supply and demand play an important part in deciding market price. When sellers are able to supply products to consumers at a price that consumers are willing to pay, a market price is found. We can say consumers demand products at this price. This market price, found when supply equals demand, satisfies both the buyer and the seller. The chart below shows supply and demand schedules for running shoes that are sold in an area where many people jog. The asterisks (*) show equal supply and demand numbers. The price shown on the line with the asterisk represents the market price.

SUPPLY SCHEDULE		DEMAND SCHEDULE	
(Products Offered)		(Products Bought)	
Price	Pairs Supplied	Price	Pairs Bought
$62.00	2,500	$62.00	750
$58.00	1,500	$58.00	800
$45.00	1,000	$45.00	850
$38.00	900*	$38.00	900*
$36.00	750	$36.00	990
$33.00	700	$33.00	1,010
$22.00	550	$22.00	2,700

*$38.00 represents the market price, or the price at which supply equals demand.

A. Circle the answer that will make each statement correct.

1. A market price is reached when supply (equals, exceeds) demand.

2. A (consumer, market) price is said to satisfy both seller and buyer.

3. The market price shown on the supply and demand schedules for the running shoes is ($38.00, $45.00)

4. At a price of $62.00, there were (700 or 2,500) pairs of running shoes demanded.

5. At a price of $22.00, there were (2,700 or 550) pairs of running shoes supplied.

6. At a price of $45.00, there were (more, less) pairs offered than pairs bought.

7. The demand schedule is concerned with products (offered, bought).

What Is a Surplus or a Shortage?

A **surplus** is more of a product than a producer can sell. Sometimes producers charge prices that are too high and the products cannot be sold at those prices. Consumer likes and dislikes can also affect the sale of products. In either case, the producer may then have a surplus of goods. In order to get rid of this surplus, the price of the product has to be lowered.

On the other hand, the consumer demand for a product may go up for any number of reasons. If the producer cannot supply enough of the product, then a **shortage** occurs. A shortage means that there is not enough of a product that consumers want to buy. Consider the case of the running shoes. If twice as many people took up jogging and wanted to buy shoes, the producer would soon run out of shoes. Other producers may offer similar shoes for sale. This may or may not change the market price, depending on the customers' willingness to buy this new brand of shoes. Prices are always changing in a market. Consumers have an important effect on the prices that can be obtained for a product or a service.

Prices—Then and Now

You have probably heard your parents or grandparents talk about how prices have gone up since they were young. Generations ago, ice cream cones cost about 10 cents. Filling up a car's gas tank cost about $1.00. Today we need a few dollars for ice cream cones, and one dollar's worth of gas wouldn't get us very far on the highway.

Another way to measure price is to think about how much labor it takes to buy certain things. For example, in 1908 a car cost most people two years' earnings. In 1997, a medium-priced car could be purchased for about eight months' earnings. In 1919, it took 39 minutes of work to buy a half-gallon of milk. Today, only seven minutes of work will buy a half-gallon of milk.

B. Read the phrases below. Choose the phrase that gives the meaning of the italicized word in each sentence. Write the phrase on the line.

• more of a product than can be sold • not enough of a good or service that consumers want to buy	• the cost of a product • amount of a product to be sold • people who buy and use goods and services

1. When the supply of a certain product is too low, a *shortage* occurs.

_____

2. When a product does not sell as well as expected, a *surplus* of the product occurs.

_____

3. Consumers will pay a certain *price* for a product. That price may become the market price.

_____

4. Producers will try to keep a *supply* of products to satisfy consumer demands.

_____

5. The likes and dislikes of *consumers* can affect the sale of products.

_____

Functions of Prices

Another function of prices is to tell the producers what goods can be made and sold at a **profit.** A profit is the amount of money left in a business after all the costs of production have been paid. When consumers show a great need or a desire for a product, such as running shoes, many producers will offer these goods. Prices will be set in the market as shown on the supply and demand chart. Then, producers can decide how much to supply at this price.

However, producers still take some risks. This is because both consumer likes and dislikes can change quickly. In a free enterprise system, any number of producers can enter the market. All of these producers then compete for the consumer's money. When businesses compete, prices are kept low, which benefits the consumers. It may be said that consumer money decides what will be produced and sold and at what price.

C. Match each term on the left with the correct phrase on the right.

_____ 1. profit   **a.** tells producers what can be sold at a profit

_____ 2. surplus   **b.** price that satisfies consumer and producer

_____ 3. market price   **c.** benefit when producers compete

_____ 4. a function of price   **d.** money that is left after all of the costs of production are paid

_____ 5. consumers   **e.** an extra amount that cannot be sold

D. Complete each of the following sentences.

1. _____ is the amount of money that a consumer must pay for a product.

2. Supply and _____ play an important part in deciding the market price.

3. Producers take risks because consumer _____ and _____ change.

4. When businesses _____ , prices are kept low.

5. Consumer _____ decides what will be produced and sold and at what price.

6. Give one reason why the price of a product might be lowered.

   _____

7. Give one reason why the consumer demand for a product might increase.

   _____

Competition in the Market Lesson 3

Competition is the rivalry among businesses for the consumer's money. Each business tries to get people to buy its products rather than those of another business. Competition among businesses in the marketplace is at the heart of a free enterprise system. The object of every business is to sell all of its products and to earn a profit.

Any number of businesses can enter a market. However, some products (such as automobiles) are too difficult and too expensive for small businesses to produce. In order to make a profit, they would have to charge a lot of money. Yet several American companies build cars. Competition does exist. However, businesses can enter some other markets more easily. It is in these markets that most competition takes place. New brands of bread or soft drinks are often available. New restaurants and video stores seem to open overnight.

A. Read the paragraphs above. Then, complete each of the following sentences with the correct word or phrase.

1. The object of every business is to sell all of its products and to _____ .

2. _____ does exist in most markets, including the automobile market.

3. Some markets can easily be entered. Give two examples.
   a. _____ b. _____

4. Competition among _____ is at the heart of a free enterprise system.

Price Competition
Some companies will cut the prices of their products. They will lower their price to just a few cents below another company's price. They hope that the increase in sales will make up for the lowered price. If this price cutting works, other stores may follow. A **price war,** with even lower prices offered, might take place. The consumer usually benefits from this price competition.

Advertising Competition
Each company tries to convince buyers that its products are better than another company's products. In order to do this, a company may place advertisements on radio and television, in newspapers and magazines, on billboards, or on the Internet. If these ads are convincing enough to sell the product, then prices will not have to be cut. Many people insist on buying name-brand products even at full price.

Quality Competition

Certain companies, such as makers of fine watches or custom-made automobiles, depend on the good reputation of their products to attract consumers. Everyone expects a gold watch to cost more than an ordinary watch. Custom-made cars, of course, cost more than other cars that do not get that special attention.

Service Competition

Many companies and businesses attract consumers by offering "extras." These extras may include free delivery, trading stamps, guarantees, or **rebates**— discounts in price. A restaurant known for its attention to customers will bring people back time after time. Twenty-four hour stores, same-day cleaning services, or overnight package delivery services will help bring customers to a business without cutting prices.

The Value and Benefit of Competition

It should seem clear that competition takes place in many forms. Many business leaders are very clever and creative in their attempts to get people to buy their products. All this competitive activity has a positive effect on a free enterprise system. Described below are four important benefits of competition.

Lower Prices

Competition keeps prices low when similar products are offered for sale. When other things are equal, such as the quality of the product, the consumer will buy the product with the lowest price. For example, a consumer may want to buy whole wheat bread. All the labels show that the ingredients in two different loaves are the same. The loaves of bread are the exact same size. A consumer will then choose the bread with the lowest price.

Better Quality

If a producer can keep the price of a product equal to other similar products, but still improve the quality, more sales will result. For example, if whole wheat bread is not only made with all-natural ingredients, but also is priced the same as other brands, consumers may choose the all-natural bread.

Efficiency of Production

Businesses strive to get work done quickly and encourage employees to do their best work. In this way, more products can be made and sold. Such efforts will increase profits without raising the price of the product. Managing time and using workers well is known as **efficiency**.

Greater Quantity and Variety

Consumers are not satisfied with the same products for very long. Businesses are always trying to attract consumer money with new and interesting products. If a product becomes very popular, businesses want to produce more of that product. Consumer likes can change quickly. Businesses will conduct research to find out about consumer likes and dislikes. This helps producers to decide what type of products consumers will buy.

B. **Read the words below. Choose the word that correctly completes each sentence. Write the word on the line provided in each sentence.**

quality	research	variety	prices
consumer	competition	service	free
advertising	lower	profit	

1. In a _____ enterprise system, any business may sell its product at any price.

2. Competition will take place among businesses and will help lower _____ .

3. A business must sell its products to make a _____ .

4. The _____ among businesses can take many forms.

5. _____ is the attempt of a business to show consumers that its product is better than the rest.

6. Sometimes the _____ of a fine product, such as gold jewelry, will attract consumers no matter what the price.

7. Two examples of _____ competition are twenty-four hour stores and free delivery.

8. Competition among several businesses always benefits the _____ .

9. _____ prices and better quality of products are two benefits to the consumer when businesses compete.

10. Another result of competition is a greater _____ of products to choose from.

11. Wise producers will conduct _____ to find out what consumers will or will not buy, because consumer likes and dislikes change.

Incomes Are Spent in the Market

Most People Earn Wages and Salaries

The market system could not work at all if people did not have the money to buy goods and services. Most people receive as income the money they later spend. Income is the payment made to an individual worker by a business. People receive this income for the work they do, or for the service they perform. Most workers receive their incomes as **wages** or salaries. A wage is usually paid per hour of work. A salary is paid for a longer period of time, such as a week, month, or year. Wages and salaries are the most common forms of income earned by American citizens.

Some workers are paid by the hour.

Some workers earn yearly salaries.

Business Income From Profits

There are other sources of income for citizens. Small businesses may be run by a single person, called an entrepreneur. They may also be run by more than one person. This business is called a **partnership.** Entrepreneurs receive their incomes as part of the profit they earn. Profit is the money left after all the costs of running a business are paid.

Rental Income

Income may also come from the **rent** a person receives for letting another person use land or property. Rent is the money one person pays for the use of someone else's property.

Interest Income From Savings or Stocks

Another source of income for some people is **interest** income. Interest is money paid to an individual who lends money to others. A bank or other financial company will pay interest to a person who puts money into an account. This interest payment is possible because the bank uses the money that was put into an account by lending it to others or by making **investments.** In turn, these investments earn money for the bank. Interest paid to the person who put the money into the account comes from this money earned by the bank. If a person has a savings account, that person's money will earn interest income from the bank.

Stockholders are people who invest their money in businesses by buying stocks. If a business is successful and earns a profit, the stockholder (owner of the stock) will receive money called a **dividend.** A dividend is a payment made to the stockholder by the business and is a form of interest income.

A. Match each word on the left with the correct definition on the right.

_____ 1. income   **a.** money earned from a savings account

_____ 2. salary   **b.** payment made to a stockholder

_____ 3. wage   **c.** money left after the cost of running a business is paid

_____ 4. interest   **d.** paid for each hour of work

_____ 5. rent   **e.** paid by the week, month, or year

_____ 6. dividend   **f.** business payment made to an individual worker for work

_____ 7. profit   done or for services performed

_____ 8. entrepreneurs   **g.** payment made for the use of someone's property

_____ 9. partnership   **h.** own and operate their own businesses

_____ 10. stockholders   **i.** people who invest money in a business by buying stock

    j. a business owned by more than one person

B. Read the words in the box. Then, read each situation. Each one describes the type of income earned by a person. Choose the word from the box which describes each type of income. Write that word on the line provided. You will use some answers more than once.

| salary | wage | dividends |
| interest | rent | business income |

1. Eva Walters once worked in a bakery, but now she runs a catering service in her home. She provides food for small private parties. She is doing very well, and her business is making money. _____

2. Tom Foley works as a gas station attendant. He started working there in high school for $6.50 per hour. He now works full time and has been given a raise of $0.75 per hour.

   _____

3. When Bob Smith's grandfather died, he left money to Bob. Bob decided to invest the money in stocks. The income from these stocks is paying for his son's college tuition.

   _____

4. After she graduated from college with training in computer programming, Laura went to work for a large corporation at $30,000 a year. She is very satisfied with her new position and is looking forward to a raise next year. _____

5. Mr. Noble owns a small building. It includes his grocery store and his apartment. This year he is planning to stop working and will let someone else use the building and the apartment. The money that he earns in this way will help him to have enough income to support his family. _____

6. Jane Carroll is a secretary who carefully saves part of her paycheck each month. She puts this money into a savings account. She receives money for keeping her money in the bank. _____

7. Tom Jackson is a teacher in a large city high school. Every year he signs an agreement that says he will work for a specified amount of money. _____

8. Alan Richards is self-employed. He has a home improvement company and does both carpentry and plumbing repairs. _____

A. Complete each of the following sentences correctly.

1. Any place where buying and selling is done is a _____ .

2. Most businesses _____ with each other in order to sell their products and make a profit.

3. One way to compete is by _____ in newspapers and on television to tell buyers about products.

4. Some businesses offer better _____ products, such as automobiles and jewelry.

5. Other businesses offer better _____ , such as free delivery or longer store hours.

6. Consumers spend the _____ they earn in the market.

7. _____ and _____ are the two most common forms of income.

8. People who lend property to others earn _____ income.

B. Match the type of competition on the left with the correct phrase on the right.

_____ 1. advertising	a. "Open 24 hours, seven days a week"
_____ 2. price	b. "Made from pure wool"
_____ 3. quality	c. "Be smart: buy Crispy Cereal."
_____ 4. service	d. "Big Sale! Two for $9.99!"

C. Read the paragraph below. Then match the type of income on the left with the description of the person who receives that income on the right.

Harry Jones owns and operates a small dry cleaning store, but he does not own the building where his business is located. He has hired someone to run the business during the day.

_____ 1. business income	a. owner of Harry's Dry Cleaners
_____ 2. wage	b. building owner
_____ 3. rental income	c. day manager of Harry's Dry Cleaners

Freedoms in a Free Enterprise System Lesson 1

Freedom to Own Private Property

Private property is anything a person owns. The American free enterprise system is based on the fact that people may own and manage their own property. It is illegal for one individual to take away another person's private property.

Most people take pride in the things they own. Property that is well cared for will increase in value and, therefore, increase the owner's wealth. A well-run business will usually earn a profit and grow. It is basic to the American free enterprise system to use private property carefully and wisely.

Freedom of Choice in Jobs and Spending Money

People have many job choices in a free enterprise system. They may apply for work anywhere and try to succeed at any job. When people earn money from their jobs, they may spend this money any way they choose. Money may be spent on basic needs or things used for enjoyment.

Consumers need to make wise choices. The government sees to it that consumers have opportunities to choose wisely. It passes laws about the ways products are made and sold. Companies must obey these laws and also be truthful in the way they advertise their products and services.

Freedom to Produce and Sell Products

All people in the United States are free to start their own businesses. They can make or sell any products they choose or offer any services, as long as the laws of the country are followed. There are millions of small businesses run by individuals or by small groups. The government cannot tell these businesses how much to charge for what they produce. If prices are too high, then consumers will not buy what is offered for sale. A company will have to lower its prices or go out of business.

A. Directions: List three freedoms that people have in a free enterprise system.

1. Freedom to _____

2. Freedom to _____

3. Freedom to _____

The Role of the Consumer

What Influence Do Consumers Have on the Economy?

Millions of families live in the United States. Most members of these families spend money. They are consumers. They buy and use the goods and services produced in the United States. In fact, consumers spend most of their incomes on goods and services. All of the ideas that you have studied in this book involve consumers. Prices are set to make these consumers want to spend their money. Businesses advertise to attract consumers. When prices are right and advertising works well, consumer spending will be high. This spending means that more people will have jobs. The money earned from these jobs is later spent. Such spending of money allows businesses to grow as products are improved and more people are employed. The whole economy improves when consumers spend money. Less consumer spending means a slowdown in the economy.

The Consumer's Role Has Changed in Modern Times

In the United States today, a consumer must be well informed and educated about products to make the best use of money. Some products, such as computers, are not always easy to understand. It is difficult to know which computer might be the best one to buy. Advertising can also make buying difficult. Businesses make many claims about their products. A television ad may tell you that the use of a certain product can make you more popular, smarter, younger looking, or happier. These claims are not always true. Consumers should use good judgment and get enough information before they buy any product. An honest company will supply all the needed information to consumers if they ask. The government will also give the consumer information about products or businesses. In the United States, laws exist to control the quality and safety of most products. However, some businesses do not always follow the rules.

Consumers Show Approval With Their Money

When consumers spend money on a certain product, they are showing their approval. This purchase shows producers what customers want and what they are willing to spend their money on. If producers want to earn profits, they pay attention to consumer approval and supply these products for sale. The success or failure of a business can depend on consumer spending.

CONSUMER SPENDING

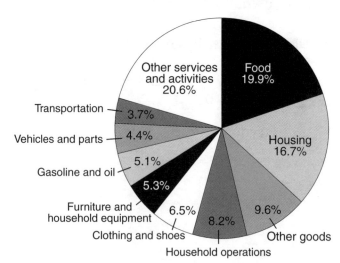

Other services and activities 20.6%

Transportation 3.7%

Vehicles and parts 4.4%

Gasoline and oil 5.1%

Furniture and household equipment 5.3%

Clothing and shoes 6.5%

Household operations 8.2%

Other goods 9.6%

Housing 16.7%

Food 19.9%

Advertising Is Used to Influence Consumers

Advertising is the main way businesses get consumers to buy their products. Businesses try to convince consumers that their own products are better than all others.

In the automobile industry, for example, advertising is used to convince people that they cannot do without a new car. Every few years, cars become better built, sleeker, and more efficient. Other businesses use the same means: bigger and better televisions, louder stereos, the newest clothing styles, and better appliances that consumers "can't live without." Businesses spend a lot of money on advertising because it works. As a result, consumers spend their money to purchase the advertised products. The spending of consumer money is a very necessary part of the American economy.

A. Complete each of the following sentences. You may refer to the circle graph on page 32.

1. _____ claims can make buying difficult for consumers because the claims may not always be true.

2. Consumers spend _____ percent of their money on housing and _____ percent on food.

3. When consumer spending is high, _____ can grow as products are improved.

4. A consumer can get information about products from the _____ itself or from the _____ .

5. In the United States, the government makes _____ to control the quality and safety of products.

6. Customers show approval of a product when they _____ to buy that product.

7. _____ is the main method used by businesses to get consumers to buy their products.

8. Consumer spending must be kept _____ in order to sell products.

9. _____ spend a lot of money on advertising in order to sell products.

10. Consumers spend their money to purchase the _____ products.

Types of Businesses

Three Basic Types of Businesses

The market economy of the United States includes more than 20 million businesses. These businesses are divided into three main types: **sole proprietorships,** partnerships, and **corporations.** Individuals are free to start any type of business they wish if they have the money. Let us look at these three basic types of businesses.

Sole Proprietorship

A sole proprietorship is a business owned by one person. This person may have many employees. Although about 73 percent of all the businesses in the United States are sole proprietorships, they account for only 16 percent of all sales of goods and services. This single owner of a business is said to have **unlimited liability,** which means the owner is held responsible for all debts of the company. This person can lose not only company money but also personal money and property.

Partnership

A partnership is a business owned by two or more people, or partners, who share the tasks of running the business. Usually, the partners write a **contract,** which is a legal document. When the partners sign the contract, they must then follow the rules that were included in the contract. Each partner usually agrees to supply some of the capital, which is the money needed to set up and operate the business. The partners will also decide how to share the profits. If one partner dies or wants to leave the business, the contract will have the rules that must be followed to do this.

As with a single-owner business, a partnership may have unlimited liability. Unless a special contract is issued, the partners may lose personal property and money as a result of a failed business.

Corporation

A corporation is a business owned by more than one person. The difference between a partnership and a corporation is in the way the corporation is set up. If the owners of a business want to turn it into a corporation, they must get permission from the state. The state will then issue the business a **charter** that makes it a legal corporation. This corporation then can act as an individual person by doing such things as making contracts, borrowing money, and buying and selling property—all in the name of the corporation. Corporations are the most important form of businesses. Eighty-nine percent of all products and services sold in the United States come from corporations.

Limited Liability Protects the Owners

The main advantage of a corporation is given to the owners. The owners have **limited liability,** which means that they cannot lose personal property if the corporation fails. The owners can lose only the money which they have put into the business. All this is written into the charter of a corporation and protected by the law.

Corporations Sell Shares

To raise money, corporations will sell small shares of their company to people who want to invest. Each person who buys a share is called a stockholder and receives a **stock certificate** that includes his or her name and the number of shares owned. If the corporation is successful and earns money, the stockholders, along with the owners, share in the profits. Corporations are the only kind of businesses that can sell stocks publicly.

THREE TYPES OF BUSINESSES

Type of Business	Advantages	Disadvantages
Sole Proprietorship (73 percent of total)	• Easy to organize • Owner receives all proceeds after taxes • Own boss	• Limited money to improve and expand • No one to share losses with • Unlimited liability • Must be good at managing, selling, and producing
Partnership (7 percent of total)	• Easy to organize but needs a contract • Can share risks • Easier to borrow money • More skills available	• Profits must be shared • Losses shared—one partner may have more to lose • Hard to dissolve if only one partner leaves • Unlimited liability
Corporation (20 percent of total)	• Very easy to borrow money • Lose only money invested (limited liability) • Easy to sell ownership by selling stocks • Accounts for 89 percent of all sales	• Extra taxes and government rules • Special rules for buying and selling stocks • Little owner control with many stockholders

A. **Write the correct facts under each column below.**

• 73 percent of all businesses   • about 89 percent of all sales
• stockholders own shares   • limited money to expand
• difficult to dissolve   • partners may lose possessions
• limited liability   • own boss
• about 20 percent of businesses   • single unlimited liability
• least common type (7 percent)   • needs a contract

Sole Proprietorship   **Corporation**   **Partnership**

_____   _____   _____

_____   _____   _____

_____   _____   _____

_____   _____   _____

B. **Circle the word or phrase that correctly completes each sentence.**

1. (Corporations, Partnerships) are the most important form of business in the United States.

2. A (sole proprietorship, partnership) is a business owned by one person.

3. Most partnerships write a (stock, contract) that sets down the rules for the business to follow.

4. If a business has unlimited liability, the owners (are, are not) personally responsible for all of the debts.

5. The state will issue a corporation a (stock, charter), which is a legal document.

6. A corporation has limited liability, which means that the owners (can, cannot) lose personal property if the corporation fails.

7. Each person who buys a share of the corporation's stock is known as a (partner, stockholder).

Corporations sell stocks at the New York Stock Exchange.

The Role of Business

Business Goal: To Make a Profit

All businesses, large and small, have a common goal: to make a profit. A **normal profit** is needed for companies to stay in business. A normal profit is the smallest amount of profit necessary to keep a business operating. Most businesses want more than a normal profit. The larger the profit, the more the business grows. Large profits mean that a business can hire more employees, make more products, or even construct a new building or factory.

Businesses Are Both Producers and Consumers

As producers, businesses supply the goods and services that people buy. In order to produce goods and services, businesses themselves need to buy certain other goods and services. Businesses then act as consumers. For example, a new automobile from a factory started as a natural resource, iron ore. This iron had to be mined from the ground, made into steel at a steel plant, and then purchased by the automobile plants. Only then could the steel be used to make the new car. Human labor, as well as machines and tools, were used at both the steel and automobile plants. A company, such as the automobile business, acts as a consumer first. Then, it can make a product for sale.

Functions of Business

One function of business is to create jobs. Businesses employ millions of people and provide them with incomes to spend on goods and services. Another function of business is to help pay for the cost of running the government. Businesses pay taxes to the federal and local governments. Just as individuals pay taxes on their incomes, so do all businesses.

Business Responsibilities

A **responsibility** is a duty, or the right thing to do. The chart below shows the responsibilities involved in business.

BUSINESS RESPONSIBILITIES	
Responsible to	**Examples of Responsibilities**
Workers	Safety on the job; fair wage
Owners	Earn profits; improve the business
Consumers	Truth in advertising; good service and products
Society	Equal job opportunities for women and minorities
Environment	No pollution of water, air, or land

A. Read the paragraph about the Royal Athletic Wear Company. Then read the following statements that describe how the company acts in a responsible way toward various groups of people. Decide which group from the box is affected by each statement. Write the name of the correct groups on the lines provided. You may use a group more than once.

The Royal Athletic Wear Company makes athletic wear, such as warm-up suits, sweatshirts, and sweatpants. It employs about 250 people. The employees work in two shifts on heavy-duty sewing machines. They are paid according to the amount of work they finish during their shifts. This is a responsible business and seems to be fair to its employees.

Workers	Society	Owners	Consumers

1. All material used in the clothing is pre-shrunk and 100 percent fireproof. _____

2. Both dental and medical insurance are offered at a lower price to employees. _____

3. Safety goggles are provided to all employees. _____

4. The company hires many employees from minority groups. _____

5. Well-trained salespeople keep sales and profits high. _____

6. Money-back guarantees are offered to buyers if clothing is found to be faulty. _____

The Role of Organized Labor

What Is Organized Labor?

Labor usually refers to the work that people do. American workers are an important part of the labor force. **Organized labor** refers to those workers in business who have joined together to form **labor unions.** Labor unions are groups of workers whose main purpose is to protect their own economic interests: wages, hours, and working conditions.

The United States did not always have labor unions to protect its workers. Members of labor unions pay dues. Many unions have become huge and powerful over the years. The American Federation of Labor (AFL) and Congress of Industrial Organizations (CIO) are two labor unions that joined together after many years of being separate unions.

Development of Labor Unions

In the late 1700s, certain craft workers—printers, shoemakers, and carpenters— joined together in groups. They were fighting against pay cuts, long working hours, and unsafe working conditions. Some of these small craft unions failed. The ones that succeeded joined together in 1881. In 1886 they became known as the American Federation of Labor (AFL). Samuel Gompers was the leader of the AFL for the next forty years.

Although these craft workers were organized, there were still other large groups of unskilled workers who were not organized. They worked in industries such as steel, automobile, rubber, and other mass-production industries. It was not until the 1930s that some of these unskilled workers were organized. A man named John L. Lewis was an early organizer of the coal miners. They had difficulty organizing at first. Finally, in 1935, they formed the Committee for Industrial Organization. In 1938, the name was changed to Congress of Industrial Organizations (CIO).

By 1942, the CIO had more than forty national groups. These included the automobile and steel workers. By 1955, the AFL and CIO had joined forces to form the strong union that it is today. The AFL-CIO realized that the goals of both unions were the same, and that they could be stronger as one group.

In organized labor, workers join together to form unions.

A. Complete each of the following sentences.

1. Another name for the work that people do is _____ .

2. _____ are groups of workers who join together to protect their common interests.

3. The first leader of the AFL was _____ .

4. _____ was one group of craft workers who formed one of the earliest unions.

5. _____ was the leader of the coal miners who organized unskilled workers.

6. _____ and _____ workers were two groups of unskilled workers who organized to form labor unions.

7. In _____ , the AFL and the CIO joined together to form the AFL-CIO.

What Do Labor Unions Do?

In the early years of labor unions, **riots** took place. A riot is a violent disturbance. The **strike** became the most powerful weapon of the unions. A strike means that workers refuse to work until their employers meet certain demands. Striking workers may try to keep others from working by forming **picket lines.** This is when workers parade near a factory or business, usually carrying signs that tell why they are striking.

These activities caused labor unions to become unpopular with the public and with employers. The employers did not like labor unions. Some made their workers sign a paper saying that they would not join a union. Such a paper was called a "yellow-dog contract." Some employers **blacklisted** workers who belonged to unions. Other employers would not hire the people on this blacklist. All these actions of employers failed to stop labor unions.

In the 1920s, Congress passed laws that helped the unions. One new law said that yellow-dog contracts were illegal. Another law, the Wagner Act (passed in 1935), gave workers the right to organize and to bargain with their employers. This is called **collective bargaining.** Collective bargaining became the most important work of a labor union. A strike was used only if the bargaining did not work.

THE LARGEST UNIONS IN THE UNITED STATES

Membership	Union
2,400,000	National Education Association
1,400,000	International Brotherhood of Teamsters
1,400,000	United Food and Commercial Workers International Union
1,300,000	American Federation of State, County, and Municipal Employees
1,300,000	Service Employees International Union
940,000	American Federation of Teachers
775,000	United Automobile, Aerospace, and Agricultural Implement Workers of America
750,000	Laborers' International Union of North America
750,000	International Brotherhood of Electrical Workers
700,000	United Steelworkers of America

GROWTH OF THE UNITED STATES LABOR FORCE, 1900–1998

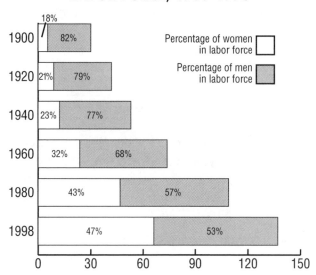

How Does Collective Bargaining Work?

If all the members of a worker's union at a certain plant decide that their wages are too low, they may ask their union for help. The leaders of the union would call a meeting with the plant managers to discuss higher wages. The union would give all of the reasons for increasing wages. The management of the plant would then present their views. If the two sides cannot reach an agreement on a fair wage, then the workers might threaten to strike.

Although union and management may have very different views, they do have a common goal: to stay in business. If the management feels that higher wages will put the company out of business, then another agreement acceptable to both sides must be reached. The workers need their jobs. Maybe some other benefit other than higher wages will be given to the workers as a result of the collective bargaining. Usually, both sides reach an agreement as a result of the talks.

B. Read the two charts above. Then, answer the questions.

1. Which union has the largest membership? _____

2. How many unions have more than one million members? _____

3. Which of the unions listed has 700,000 members? _____

4. What percentage of the labor force were women in 1980? _____

5. What percentage of the labor force were women in 1900? _____

6. Were there more men or women in the labor force in 1940? _____

7. What percentage of the labor force were men in 1960? _____

Review Unit 3

A. Choose a term below to complete each statement.

strike	picket line	yellow-dog contracts
collective bargaining	blacklist	Wagner Act

1. The _____ was a law that gave workers the right to bargain with their employers.

2. If a worker was placed on a _____ for belonging to a union, other employers would not hire that worker.

3. During a _____ , workers might form picket lines to prevent others from working.

4. Workers were sometimes forced to sign _____ in which they said that they would not join a union.

5. _____ became the most important work of a labor union.

6. A _____ is formed near the factory or place of business to prevent others from working.

B. Match each term on the left with the correct definition on the right.

_____ 1. free enterprise   **a.** created by businesses for people

_____ 2. sole proprietorship   **b.** passed by government; some are helpful to unions

_____ 3. partnership   **c.** just enough profit to stay in business

_____ 4. collective bargaining   **d.** a one-owner business

_____ 5. jobs   **e.** began organizing in the 1700s

_____ 6. laws   **f.** allows citizens to own property or to operate a business

_____ 7. normal profit   **g.** owners have unlimited liability

_____ 8. corporation   **h.** union employees bargain with employers for what they want

_____ 9. labor unions

_____ 10. high-quality products   **i.** owners can lose only money put into the business (limited liability)

      j. a responsibility of business

Reasons for Economic Growth Lesson 1

Is Economic Growth Important?

The growth of a country's economy is important for the well-being of its citizens. **Economic growth** refers to the increase in the amount of goods and services produced in a country. Overall, the American economy has grown steadily over the years because businesses have grown and improved. This economic growth provides jobs for people who become consumers with money to spend. The flow of money from consumers to businesses to employees is necessary for a healthy, working economy. If businesses lose money or fail, jobs are lost and spending stops. All of these events would slow down the growth of the economy.

Three Reasons for Economic Growth

There are three main reasons why the American economy has grown so rapidly over the years. One reason is a large supply of natural resources, such as land, water, oil, and trees. Another is a steady increase in population, which provides many workers. Some people think that a third reason, the free enterprise system, is the main reason for the rapid growth. A free enterprise system provides a variety of jobs. It also provides the opportunity to "be your own boss" by starting your own business. In a free enterprise system, most people are able to find work in which they can succeed.

Technology Has Also Helped Economic Growth

Technology is the use of scientific knowledge, especially in industry and trade. It is used to improve the way in which products are made. It has helped make better cars, televisions, appliances, electronic equipment, and computers. New machines and ways to use them have cut down on the cost of making products. This savings is passed on to consumers through lower prices. The use of computers in businesses, homes, and schools is growing rapidly. Even food has been improved by the use of technology. Better methods of growing crops and caring for animals are the results of improvements in technology. Without technology, there could be very little economic growth.

A. Choose the correct definition from the box for the italicized term in each sentence. Write the definition below the sentence.

• allows people to find work in which they can succeed	• things found in nature: land, water, oil, trees	• increase in the amount of goods and services	• use of scientific knowledge in trade and industry

1. *Economic growth* is important to the well-being of a country's citizens.

    _____

2. The United States has a large supply of *natural resources.*

    _____

3. The *free enterprise system* is a main reason for economic growth.

    _____

4. Economic growth could not take place without the use of *technology.*

    _____

The Gross National Product

The growth of the American economy is measured yearly. The total dollar value of all goods and services (such as cars, houses, and repairs) is added up. This total is called the **Gross National Product (GNP).** In some years, certain products will sell better than in other years. Businesses rely on the GNP to know what to expect in the way of future sales of their products or services. Companies can tell what products are selling well. This knowledge helps businesses to decide what and how much to produce in the future.

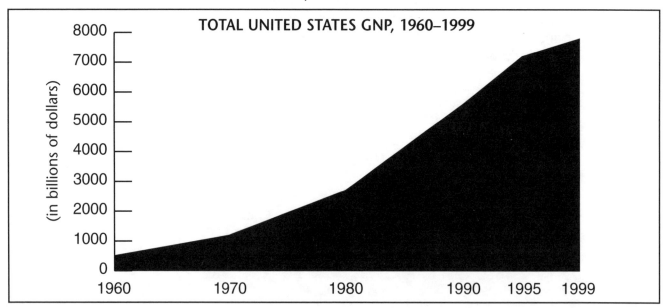

The Uneven Growth of the American Economy

Growth of the economy is necessary for the well-being of the United States. Both citizens and businesses do well when the economy improves and grows. People today have more material goods than their parents and grandparents did. The economy has improved for the good of most citizens. However, this improvement has not taken place at a steady rate. There have been many economic ups and downs. Sometimes the growth has been rapid, as in the 1920s following World War I. This rapid growth did not last.

In the 1930s, there was an economic slowdown. **Unemployment** (being without a job) was high, and people lost faith in the banking system. Because they were afraid of losing their money, people rushed to the banks to take out all that they had saved. Banks could not pay out all this money at one time. Many banks failed. Large numbers of people lost their life savings. This period in American history became known as the **Great Depression.** It lasted until the 1940s. In the 1940s, during and after World War II, the economy improved again. The economy does not remain the same for long.

B. Complete the exercise below.

1. How often is the American economy's growth measured? _____

2. What does GNP stand for? _____

3. The GNP is the total dollar value of all the _____ and

   _____ .

4. The GNP helps _____ to know what to expect in the way of future sales.

5. People today have more _____ than their parents did.

6. The _____ was a period in American history when unemployment was high and many banks failed.

7. The economy began to _____ in the 1940s, during and after World War II.

U
N
I
T

4

What Is a Business Cycle?
Economists refer to the series of changes in the American economy as the **business cycle.** A business cycle usually goes from one period of **prosperity** (good times) to the next period of prosperity.

During a period of prosperity, most people have jobs, and spending is high. Businesses are able to sell almost all they produce, which allows them to grow. All of this causes the GNP to grow during the years of prosperity. Within this business cycle, economists use the following terms to explain the cycles.

A **recession** is a gradual slowdown in business activity and consumer spending. Jobs are harder to find because businesses are not growing. Jobs are not available. Therefore, there is less money to spend on goods and services.

If the recession continues, business activity slows down even more. More people lose jobs. Both of these cause a greater slowdown, or **depression,** in the economy. **Poverty,** or lack of money, can become widespread. Serious measures to correct this must be taken by the government. For instance, during the Great Depression of the 1930s, the government tried to help the poor by setting up soup kitchens and shelters for homeless people.

Recovery is a time when business starts to improve. Employers are able to offer jobs to more people. People begin spending money, and the economy improves. The GNP will begin to rise during the years of recovery from a depression or a recession.

Breadlines like this one, and other places where people waited to get food, were common during the Great Depression.

BUSINESS CYCLES DURING THE 1900s

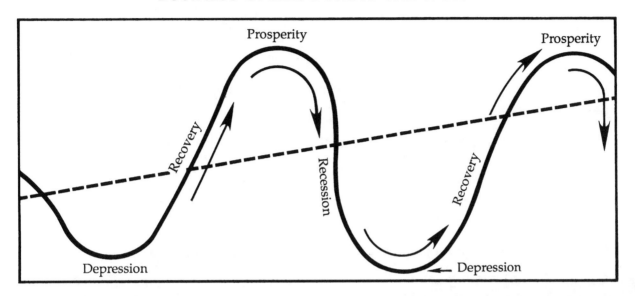

The curved line shows the uneven growth in business cycles marked by depression, recovery, prosperity, and then a recession. The dotted line represents average growth rate. It shows that growth does happen over the years, even though the yearly growth is not steady.

Why Do Business Cycles Take Place?
There are several reasons why business cycles happen and the economy changes. Such changes cannot be avoided, but economists are always trying to think of ways to make the economy more stable. Here are three important conditions that cause changes in the American economy.

First, consumers can change their demands. Businesses will rush to make the goods and to offer the services that people want.

Second, businesses may change their willingness to grow and expand. Businesses cannot spend the same amount on improvements every year. When they slow down, so does the economy. Jobs are lost and spending stops.

Finally, changes occur in interest rates charged to borrow money. The government has some control over the state of the economy. When growth seems to be too fast, the government can raise interest rates. It is then harder for businesses and individuals to borrow money. On the other hand, if there seems to be a slowdown, interest rates are lowered to encourage spending.

A. Complete each sentence with the correct term from the box.

recession	depression	interest	spending	jobs
GNP	businesses	poor	consumer	government

1. A _____ is a gradual slowdown that usually takes place after a period of prosperity.

2. The government may raise _____ rates if growth seems to be too fast.

3. Many people may lose their _____ during a depression.

4. The government had to take care of the _____ by providing food and shelter during the Great Depression.

5. If a recession goes on for a long time, it may lead to a _____ .

6. Changes in the economy can be caused by changes in _____ demands.

7. _____ will rush to make what consumers will buy.

8. Consumer _____ is high during a period of prosperity.

9. The _____ is the total value of all goods and services sold in one year.

10. The _____ has control over the interest rates charged to borrow money.

The Problem of Inflation

Inflation is a problem that sometimes occurs in the American economy. It takes place when prices rise quickly, but incomes do not rise as fast. During a time of inflation, the value of the dollar is down. For example, suppose a person has $60 a week to spend on entertainment. This person likes to buy CDs, which cost $15 each. The person can buy four CDs. One year later, the price of a CD goes up to $16, but the person's income does not rise. Then, the person can buy only three CDs with $60. People on fixed incomes, such as **retired** persons (people who are no longer working), or disabled people, see little rise in their incomes. Sometimes people are forced to live with less goods and services than they need.

Inflation is a difficult problem to change. Sometimes the government tries to control inflation with **wage and price freezes.** This action means that prices and wages must stay as they are for a while, as if frozen. The government has to approve any further rise in prices or wages. These controls are used only for a short time. Sometimes they do not help to stop inflation.

B. Write the correct answer to each of the following questions.

1. What problem occurs in the American economy due to fast-rising prices?

   _____

2. What groups of people seldom see a rise in their incomes?

   _____

3. How does the government try to control inflation?

   _____

Consumer Price Index

The **Consumer Price Index (CPI)** is a measure of the changes in the prices of goods and services from year to year. The CPI measures the prices of about 400 consumer items. By studying the CPI, consumers and businesses can see which prices are changing the fastest. This chart compares the percent increase or decrease in the cost of food and beverages from 1970 to 1999. It uses 1982 as a base year for comparison. For example, a certain food may have cost $1.00 in 1982. The same item cost $1.65 in 1999, and just 40¢ in 1970. Here is another way to compare the cost of food and beverages: A trip to the grocery store in 1970 cost $40. In 1982, it cost $100 to buy the same groceries, and in 1999 it cost $165. The money spent for the same amount of groceries more than tripled in almost 30 years. In order to keep up with the rising prices, a person's income would also have to triple in that same amount of time.

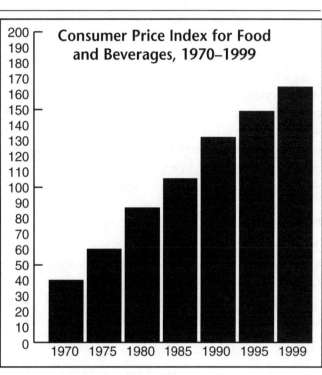

Consumer Price Index for Food and Beverages, 1970–1999

C. Read the paragraph and chart above. Then, complete the exercise.

1. A trip to the grocery store that cost $40 in 1970, cost how much in 1985?

   _____

2. How much did the same groceries cost in 1990? _____

3. Which groups of people can benefit from studying the CPI?

   _____ and _____

4. How many consumer items are used to determine the CPI? _____

5. In order to keep up with rising prices, a person's _____ also has to rise.

U
N
I
T

4

What Is Money?

Money is something given in exchange for goods or services. People did not always use the **currency,** coins and paper money, we know today. Some early forms of money were shells, stones, animal teeth, or even special foods such as spices, tea, or salt.

Another type of exchange was **bartering.** People who bartered traded something that they had for something that they wanted. If a farmer needed lumber to build a barn, the farmer could trade wheat to get it. Corn or rice might be traded for fish, furs, or tools.

Checks are another form of currency. When a person puts money into a checking account in a bank, he or she can then pay bills or purchase goods by writing checks. A check is an order to a bank to pay a certain amount of money to another person or place of business. Checks are used in place of money. Many consumers use **credit cards** as well as **cash** and checks. They must show businesses or banks that they are able to pay for the things they buy. When a person charges on a credit card, the bill must be paid later. Some credit cards charge a fee when the amount owed is not paid in full each month.

Functions of Money

Money is a **medium of exchange,** which means it is accepted by most people as payment for goods or services. Money also is a **measure of value.** Dollars, quarters, dimes, nickels, and pennies serve as units in which the worth of goods or services can be measured. The worth of these goods or services can then be compared. This worth is shown as a price. For example, an automobile might be worth $15,000; a book, $15; or a candy bar, 75¢.

Finally, money is a **store of value.** People can save or store their money to use in the future. They know that it will be accepted at any time as payment. Saving money is not the only way in which people prepare for the future. Anything of value can be used as savings, such as stocks, land, or houses. However, most people prefer money. One reason is that money is always ready to be used to pay bills or to buy what is needed. Other valuable items have to be sold or changed into money in some way before they can be used for purchases.

A. Choose the correct term from the box to fill in each blank.

medium of exchange	measure of value	store of value
bartering	credit cards	checks
currency	substitute	compare

1. Money is a _____ and is accepted as payment for goods and services.

2. Money may be in the form of _____ or _____ .

3. Checks are a _____ for money.

4. People may also pay for items by charging with _____ .

5. Years ago, people used a _____ or trading system to get what they needed.

6. People can _____ goods and services by their price. This _____ is one function of money.

7. Another function of money is that it can be used as a _____ . People can use it at any time to pay bills or to buy things.

What Is the Function of Banks?

It is almost impossible to be an active citizen of the United States without having some contact with a bank. Banks keep money safe. Banks have two main functions.

First, banks accept **deposits.** People deposit, or put, money into a bank for safe keeping and convenience. Deposits placed into a checking account can be withdrawn at any time. These are called **demand deposits** because the money can be demanded, or taken out, at any time. Money can also be deposited into and taken out of a savings account at any time. Usually banks pay interest on savings account deposits. Some banks are now also paying interest on money in checking accounts.

Second, banks make **loans.** This is the most important function of banks. Loans are made to individuals and to businesses. When banks lend money, they charge interest, or a percentage of the loan, as a fee. Interest, as well as the money borrowed, must be repaid to the bank. For example, a loan of $100 at 10 percent yearly interest means that the borrower must repay the bank $110 by the end of one year.

Banks Must Earn Profits

Commercial banks are ones used by most citizens and businesses. Just like other companies, commercial banks must earn profits to stay in business. They do this by making loans. The interest they charge on these loans provides the needed profits. This is the main way in which banks can earn income.

Banks "Create" Money by Making Loans

Loans help banks to earn profits, and they keep the economy healthy. When individuals and businesses need to borrow money, a bank "creates" this money for them. For example, if someone needs $2,500 to buy a car, that person can go to the bank for a loan. The bank checks to see if the person has income from a job and can pay the loan back. The bank also checks to see if the person has any other loans, or has borrowed much in the past. When the bank agrees to make the loan, the person must sign a **promissory note,** or note promising to pay back the money. The bank then gives the person the money to buy the car. Each month, the person pays a certain amount to the bank until the loan plus interest is paid off. This loan not only satisfies the needs of the car buyer, it helps the bank to earn the income it needs to stay in business. The loan also helps the economy to grow because 2,500 more dollars are being used.

B. **Decide whether each of the following phrases is concerned with** *Deposits* **or** *Loans,* **the two main functions of a bank. Write the correct word on the line provided after each phrase.**

1. keep money safe _____

2. checking accounts _____

3. savings accounts _____

4. earn interest for the bank _____

5. most important function of bank _____

6. bank earns profit _____

7. demand deposits _____

8. withdraw money anytime _____

9. earn interest for depositor _____

10. create money _____

11. checks _____

12. made to businesses _____

The Federal Reserve System

History of Banking in the United States

Banking began in early times. People known as goldsmiths kept other people's gold, silver, and other valuables in a safe place. They stored these valuables in safes and gave people slips of paper that told how much was stored. These pieces of paper could be used in place of money. These goldsmiths were the first bankers.

Banking in the United States began in colonial times. Some private banks were formed to store people's money. Many of these banks failed. In 1791, Congress founded a national bank in order to help the bankers. It failed. The second bank of 1816 failed also, after only twenty years.

Why Did the Early Banks Fail?

The early private banks issued paper money to show how much gold or silver was stored. Often, too much paper money was printed. It was not backed by gold or silver. When people tried to cash in the paper money, they found that it was worthless. This reaction caused a panic in banking and finances in 1863. Congress tried to pass measures that would end these poor banking practices, but these early laws did not help. It was not until 1913, when the government founded the **Federal Reserve System**, that banking improved. This system limited the amount of paper money that was printed. People's deposits were protected. The Federal Reserve System saved banking in the United States.

A. Write the correct answer to each of the following questions.

1. What did Congress found in 1791 in an attempt to help the bankers?

   _____

2. What did early banks print to show how much gold or silver was stored?

   _____

3. What happened in 1863 when paper money became worthless because too much of it was printed? _____

4. What was founded by the government in 1913 to improve banking?

   _____

5. The Federal Reserve System did two things to improve banking. What were they?

   a. _____

   b. _____

THE FEDERAL RESERVE SYSTEM

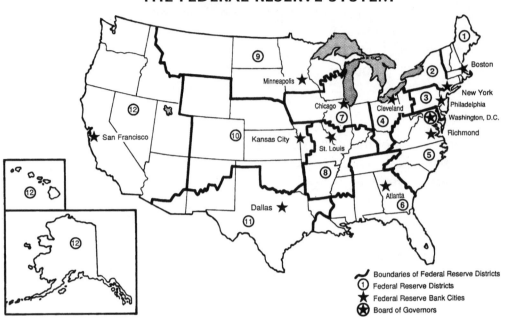

Boundaries of Federal Reserve Districts
① Federal Reserve Districts
★ Federal Reserve Bank Cities
✪ Board of Governors

What Is the Federal Reserve System?

The Federal Reserve System is the central banking system in the United States. It is the banker's banker. There are 25 Federal Reserve banks in 12 districts located throughout the country. These Federal Reserve banks do business with commercial banks and other financial institutions within their districts. Other financial institutions may include savings and loans, savings banks, and credit unions. All national banks must belong to the Federal Reserve System, but any other financial institution may join. Several thousand banks are members of the Federal Reserve System.

The Federal Reserve System Controls the Money

The Federal Reserve System offers its member banks four services and privileges. First, banks are allowed to borrow money. Second, the system keeps reserves of cash for banks and other financial institutions to draw on. Financial advice and assistance are also offered to member banks. Finally, dividends are paid on stocks bought in the district banks.

The Fed

The Federal Reserve System is often called the Fed. It is headed by a nine-member board of governors. This board, along with member banks, makes important decisions concerning the economy, such as raising or lowering interest rates. The chair of this board is a spokesperson for the Fed, and often becomes familiar to the public. Dr. Alan Greenspan has been the chair since 1987. He advises board and bank members about the country's economic matters and announces decisions to the public. These announcements affect how people borrow and use money. This influences the country's economy.

The Federal Reserve System Controls the Money Supply

The supply of money is important in a free enterprise system. If there is not enough money available for loans, the economy will not grow and improve. Too much money in circulation will cause the value of money to go down. The supply of money is closely watched and controlled by the Federal Reserve System. Each member bank must keep a certain amount of money on hand, or in reserve. This money cannot be loaned out.

The amount to be kept in reserve can be raised or lowered by the Federal Reserve System. This controls the amount of money that is in circulation, being used by businesses and individuals.

The Federal Reserve System also controls the money supply by changing the rate of interest charged to banks that want to borrow money. For example, a high interest rate will keep banks from borrowing. A bank then has less money to lend out, which lowers the money supply.

How Reserves of Banks Are Controlled

A bank must keep a percentage of its money in reserve. Most of this reserve money is kept on deposit with the Federal Reserve bank in the bank's district. Suppose the percentage of reserve is set at 20 percent. A bank that takes in a deposit of $500 would have to keep $100 ($500 x 0.20 = $100) in reserve. The bank could only lend out $400 of the $500 it took in deposit.

B. Read the terms listed in the box below. Choose seven terms that describe the Federal Reserve System. Write them on the lines provided.

central banking system	all banks belong	banker's banker
pays dividends	500 members	raises reserves
offers advice	no control of money	lowers reserves
individuals can borrow	25 districts	25 banks

Federal Reserve System

1. _____

2. _____

3. _____

4. _____

5. _____

6. _____

7. _____

Review Unit 4

A. Solve the puzzle. First, write the word that will complete each statement. Then write the words in the puzzle below.

Across words:

1. _____ resources helped the American economy grow.

2. _____ is a stable or good time financially.

3. The United States measures its economy by the Gross National _____ .

4. Money is a medium of _____ .

5. _____ accept deposits and make loans.

6. Making _____ is the most important function of banks.

7. Business _____ or periods of growth or slowdown, occur because the economy is not always steady.

8. Banking began in _____ times in the United States

9. The Federal Reserve System is the country's central _____ system.

10. _____ as we know it today, is in the form of currency and checks.

Down word:

11. _____ has also been a reason for the economic growth of the United States. It has helped to improve production, even in the way people grow food.

```
                              ┌─ 11. ─┐
                              │       │
        1.         __ __ │__│ __ __ __ __
                              │       │
        2.     __ __ __ __ __ │__│ __ __ __
                              │       │
        3.     __ __ __ __ __ │__│ __
                              │       │
        4.       __ __ __ __ __ │__│ __ __ __ __
                              │       │
        5.       __ __ │__│ __ __
                              │       │
        6.         __ │__│ __ __ __
                              │       │
        7.       __ __ __ │__│ __ __
                              │       │
        8.     __ __ __ __ │__│ __ __ __ __
                              │       │
        9.   __ __ __ __ __ __ │__│
                              │       │
       10.     __ __ __ __ │__│
                              └───────┘
```

Government Laws and Rules for Business Lesson 1

How Is the Government Involved in America's Economic System?

In America's early days, the government played only a small part in business activity. Government protected the rights of citizens, printed money, and provided a postal service. A system of courts and judges was also run by the government. In 1800, the government spent only 11 million dollars. By the late 1990s, the government was spending over a trillion dollars per year. Today, all governments (federal, state, city, and local) are completely involved in the nation's economic activity.

Businesses must work according to laws made by the government and enforced by its agencies. There are laws to guide all parts of business and industry. There are laws to protect consumers and workers. The government is also involved in the economy because of the huge sums of money that are spent at all levels of government. This lesson will show how the government controls business activities.

Government Controls Business by Passing Laws and Rules

As more businesses formed in the United States, competition became very strong and sometimes unfair. The government was forced to become involved in order to keep competition honest and fair. Such competition is important in a free enterprise system. Small businesses must be given the same chance to compete for consumer money that larger, more powerful corporations have.

A. Choose the correct term to complete each sentence. Write each answer on the line.

1. In the early days of the United States, the government provided a _____ (railroad, postal service).

2. In _____ , the government spent only 11 million dollars. (1800, 1890)

3. The government became involved in business to keep _____ fair and honest. (workers, competition)

Government Control of Monopolies

A **monopoly** is control of the production of goods or services by one business. As a result of this control, competition may end because there is only one producer of the good or service. The railroads were one of the first businesses in the country to form monopolies. In many parts of the country, there was only one railroad. Therefore, this railroad could charge any price it wanted for its services. A business or individual had to pay the price in order to ship by rail or to ride from place to place. There was no other competing railroad company to use.

The federal government felt that it was unfair for one small group to get all of the benefits from something that all of the people needed. It saw a need to pass laws to control monopolies. The following are some examples of important laws passed since that time.

Sherman Antitrust Act (1890)

Some other companies began to form monopolies in much the same way as the railroads had. The Standard Oil Company, under the leadership of John D. Rockefeller, had formed the largest monopoly at the time. In twenty years, this company had gained control of 90 percent of the country's oil business. In 1890, Standard Oil was worth 40 million dollars. The Sherman Antitrust Act broke up the monopoly into twenty smaller oil companies in order to allow competition in the oil business.

Clayton Antitrust Act (1914)

Some businesses used unfair and illegal practices. One practice was known as the **tying agreement.** Under this agreement, a seller would refuse to sell to a buyer unless the buyer bought other products also made by the company. For example, a seller of men's suits would force a buyer to buy their shirts and ties as well. Antitrust laws helped put an end to such unfair practices.

The Clayton Act also ended certain **mergers** of companies. A merger takes place when one company buys another, and the two of them become one firm. The government saw that competition was greatly reduced when companies merged.

Robinson-Patman Act (1936)

This law prevented companies from selling products to one business cheaper than it would sell the same products to another company.

B. **Choose the correct term to complete each sentence. Write each answer on the line.**

   1. The _____ were one of the first businesses to form monopolies. (oil companies, railroads)

   2. The _____ formed a monopoly broken up by the Sherman Antitrust Act. (railroad, Standard Oil Company)

   3. The _____ Act prevented companies from forming tying agreements. (Clayton, Robinson-Patman)

   4. The _____ Act prevented companies from selling products to one business more cheaply than to another. (Clayton, Robinson-Patman)

Government Agencies That Regulate Business

Sometimes large, wealthy companies keep trying to grow larger to increase profits for the stockholders. They do this by buying and merging with certain companies. Often, this goes against the Clayton Act. Very large companies can force small companies out of business. The government keeps close control over large companies to avoid such unfair growth. It must prevent monopolies and other unfair practices if honest competition is to continue. Fair competition among businesses must be allowed if the free enterprise system is to succeed.

In an effort to preserve free enterprise, the government has set up agencies to enforce the laws. These are some important government agencies:

- The Federal Trade Commission (FTC) prevents unfair competition and other illegal practices among businesses.

- The Federal Communications Commission (FCC) issues licenses to and checks on radio and TV stations. It also regulates telephone and telegraph rates and service.

- The Securities and Exchange Commission (SEC) regulates the sale of stocks and the people who sell them.

- The Federal Energy Regulatory Commission (FERC) regulates the rates, sale, and transportation of electricity and natural gas. In addition, it regulates the sale of oil transported by pipeline.

- The Environmental Protection Agency (EPA) sets up and enforces rules forbidding pollution. It also aids the government in trying to stop pollution.

C. **Match the agency above with the work it does. Write the letter abbreviation for each agency on the line.**

_____ **1.** regulates the sale and transportation of electricity

_____ **2.** tries to control pollution

_____ **3.** regulates the sale of stocks and the people who sell them

_____ **4.** licenses radio and TV stations

_____ **5.** controls unfair competition among businesses

_____ **6.** aids the government in trying to stop pollution

_____ **7.** regulates telephone and telegraph rates

_____ **8.** checks on the sale of oil transported by pipelines

Government Laws to Protect Consumers and Workers   Lesson 2

Consumers Need Protection

Consumers expect the goods they buy to be safe. They expect the services they pay for (whether education, police protection, or automobile repairs) to be of good quality. Consumers should also be able to believe advertising claims and promises. Unfortunately, some businesses have not always been honest and fair to consumers.

How Does the Government Protect Consumers?

The federal government has had to use its power to protect consumers from some unfair business practices. During the 1930s, the government set up the Consumer Advisory Board to help consumers learn about products and services. This agency was the first government agency that took care of only the interests of consumers.

Product safety and truthful advertising are two areas of business that the government watches closely. The following are some agencies set up by the government to protect consumers.

The Federal Trade Commission (FTC) protects consumers by controlling advertising. False or misleading claims about products are not allowed. This agency looks into all types of claims about products from aspirin to automobile tires.

One famous case involved a company that made diet bread. The claim was made in a television ad that this bread had fewer calories than other breads. The bread had fewer calories only because it was sliced thinner, but even then the calorie difference was very small. The FTC found this ad misleading and asked the company to change it.

The Consumer Product Safety Commission sets standards of safety for consumer products. This commission also has the power, through the law, to make sure that these standards are followed. It can force companies to take back products found to be unsafe. For example, children's toys have often been found to be unsafe.

The Food and Drug Administration (FDA) guards the safety and use of prescription drugs. It also controls the handling of food products and cosmetics. The FDA can also require that warning labels, such as "This product may be habit forming," be put on products. This agency formed soon after Upton Sinclair wrote *The Jungle* in 1906. This book described the filth and disease in the meat-packing plants of Chicago. The public was shocked, and the government moved quickly to clean up plant conditions. A meat inspection act was then passed. Soon after, the Food and Drug Administration was begun.

Besides these federal regulations, many states and even cities have set up agencies to handle consumer complaints. A private organization, the Better Business Bureau (BBB), has been set up in some areas by local companies. The BBB looks into businesses that have received many complaints about their products or services. The BBB also publishes buying guides, pamphlets, and books. These cover most products consumers buy, like clothing, automobiles, computers, CDs, and other items. Since many people are now shopping on the Internet using computers, the BBB also offers information and tips for shopping on-line.

A. **Read the phrases listed in the box below. Choose the phrase that correctly completes each of the following sentences. Write that phrase on the line provided.**

consumer complaints from the market	fair to consumers learn about products	Food and Drug Administration the meat-packing plants

1. The Consumer Product Safety Commission has the power to remove unsafe products

   _____ .

2. Businesses have not always been _____ .

3. The Consumer Advisory Board was set up to help people _____ .

4. A private organization, the Better Business Bureau, often investigates

   _____ .

5. A warning label may be put on a product by the _____ .

6. *The Jungle* told about conditions in _____ .

American Workers Now Receive Protection Through the Government
In Unit 3, you learned how the Wagner Act gave workers the right to form labor unions and to bargain with employers. This act was one of the first and most important laws passed by the government to protect workers.

The Social Security Act was also passed in 1935. It gives workers insurance against unemployment. It also assures workers that they will have an income when they retire. In 1938, the Fair Labor Standards Act was put into effect. Some of the benefits it gave workers were a **minimum wage** (the lowest amount a person can be paid), an end to child labor, and higher wages for overtime pay from companies who traded between states.

More recently, the Civil Rights Act of 1964 was passed. Part of this act concerned the hiring practices of companies. According to this law, companies cannot refuse to give a person a job on the basis of race, color, religion, national origin, or sex.

The health of workers on the job is also a concern of the government. The Occupational Safety and Health Administration (OSHA) makes sure that companies follow safety and health rules.

B. Write the correct answer to each of the following questions.

1. Name two benefits given to workers by the Fair Labor Standards Act.

   a. _____

   _____

   b. _____

   _____

The government passes laws to make sure workers are protected.

2. Which government agency makes sure that health rules are followed?

   _____

3. The Social Security Act provides income for which two groups of people?

   a. _____

   b. _____

4. Which act controls the hiring practices of businesses?

   _____

5. Which act allowed workers to form labor unions?

   _____

Government Spending

The Government Spends Money for the Good of the Public

All levels of government—federal, state, and local—spend money to provide goods and services for people. Services that can be supplied only by the government are **public goods.** Examples of public goods are highways, defense, police and fire protection, **public utilities** (electric and gas power), schools, and welfare and unemployment payments. Governments also spend money to build office buildings and pay the wages and salaries of all government employees, including the President, governors, and mayors. The government also runs the many agencies that regulate business activity and protect consumers and workers. You learned about many of these agencies in the last lesson.

Some goods and services that affect the whole country are provided only by the federal government (for example, defense). Local needs are usually provided by state, city, and other local governments.

What Goods and Services Are Provided by the Federal Government?

The federal government spends the largest amount of money on **income security,** or payments that protect people's incomes. Such payments are given to retired workers, people out of work (unemployed), and disabled people.

The second largest amount of money is spent on **national defense.** The government is in charge of all branches of the military: Army, Navy, Air Force, and Marines. Huge amounts of money are spent to supply all the needs of the defense system. These needs include weapons, ships, planes, uniforms, and wages. The government also finances research to develop weapons, nuclear energy, and the space program.

The **national debt,** or interest owed on money borrowed by the government, is the third largest category of spending. When the federal government does not have enough money to carry out its programs, it must borrow money.

The next largest amount is spent on health care for the elderly, poor, disabled, and people who have served in the military. The government trains and educates people in the field of health care, and is concerned about the safety and health of workers and consumers.

Federal spending also pays for education, **employment** (jobs), and **social services.** This area includes public and job education as well as research to develop better methods of education. Social services to take care of people in need are concerns of the federal government.

There are many other areas of spending, such as natural resources, transportation, agriculture, courts, and international matters.

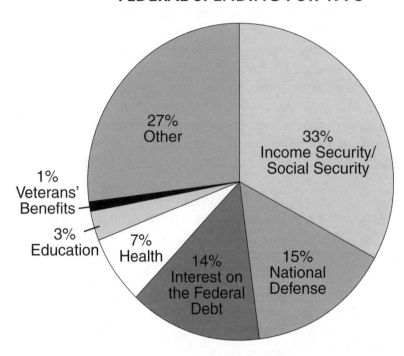

FEDERAL SPENDING FOR 1998

(Pie chart)
- 27% Other
- 33% Income Security/Social Security
- 1% Veterans' Benefits
- 3% Education
- 7% Health
- 14% Interest on the Federal Debt
- 15% National Defense

A. Read the paragraphs on page 63 and study the chart above on federal spending. Then complete each sentence with the correct term.

1. The third largest category of federal spending is _____ .

2. This third largest category amounted to _____ percent of the total spending described in the chart.

3. According to the chart, the federal government spent 14 percent of its money on

   _____ .

4. The federal government is concerned about the _____ and health of workers.

5. According to the chart, the government spent 7 percent of its money on _____ .

6. The government spends money for research in _____ to find better methods to use in schools.

7. About 27 percent of federal money was spent for other things. Two of these are

   _____ and _____ .

8. According to the chart, the least amount of money is spent on _____ .

The Federal Budget

The money that the federal government spends for the public good comes from taxes. These taxes are paid by individuals and by businesses. Before the federal government can spend any of this money, a federal **budget** must be made. A budget is a plan that tells how money will be spent. The President and other people in the government are responsible for making the federal budget. This budget is prepared for a **fiscal year,** which is a twelve-month period of financial planning. The written budget may contain hundreds of pages. It is sent to Congress, where it is carefully studied. Changes may be suggested before it is approved. This approval is needed before the money can be spent.

Goods and Services Provided by State and Local Governments

All spending by local governments must be approved by their legislatures or councils. As with the federal government, most of the money comes from taxes. Here are some of the ways in which local governments use their money:

• Most money is spent on elementary and secondary education. Some funds are spent on colleges and universities.

• Money is also spent on **public welfare.** People who earn wages considered below the poverty level receive aid from local governments.

• State governments pay for most highways. This money comes from gasoline tax and other taxes.

• Some states and cities offer retirement benefits to employees. They also give **unemployment insurance** payments to those workers who lose their jobs.

• The governments of many large cities maintain hospitals or **clinics.** Also, help is given to some private hospitals that cannot operate on just the fees that are charged to patients.

• Police protection is provided by states as well as many towns and cities within the state.

• Just as the federal government borrows money, so do local governments. The **debt interest,** or interest owed on a loan, is usually part of a state's or city's budget.

• Finally, state and local governments provide money for several other areas. This spending includes such items as fire protection, recreation areas, public parks, libraries, zoos, public water systems, and street construction and repair.

U
N
I
T

5

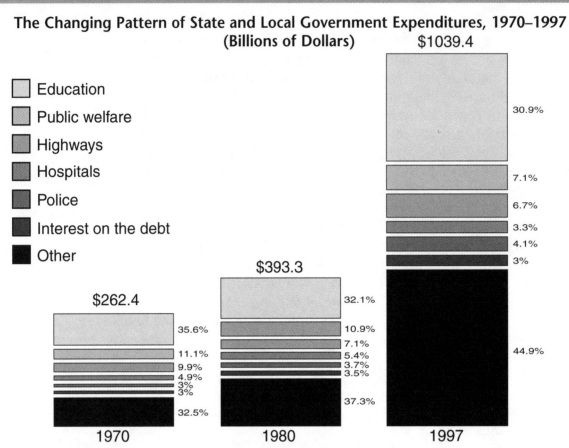

The Changing Pattern of State and Local Government Expenditures, 1970–1997 (Billions of Dollars)

Legend:
- Education
- Public welfare
- Highways
- Hospitals
- Police
- Interest on the debt
- Other

1997 — $1039.4
- 30.9%
- 7.1%
- 6.7%
- 3.3%
- 4.1%
- 3%
- 44.9%

1980 — $393.3
- 32.1%
- 10.9%
- 7.1%
- 5.4%
- 3.7%
- 3.5%
- 37.3%

1970 — $262.4
- 35.6%
- 11.1%
- 9.9%
- 4.9%
- 3%
- 3%
- 32.5%

B. Read the paragraphs on page 65 and study the chart above on state and local spending. List the first five categories of this spending. Then read the examples of local spending listed in the box. Write two examples below each category.

Central School	traffic lights	jails	patrol cars	food stamps
City Hospital	welfare checks	Highway 141	emergency room	teachers' salaries

Category 1. _____
Examples: _____

Category 2. _____
Examples: _____

Category 3. _____
Examples: _____

Category 4. _____
Examples: _____

Category 5. _____
Examples: _____

World Trade

Lesson 4

U
N
I
T

5

Products From Other Countries

Most people use and enjoy products from other countries. The United States allows other countries to sell their products to American consumers. There are two reasons why the United States needs products from other countries. Either the United States cannot make the product as cheaply, or it is not possible to produce the product at all. For example, the United States does not have the right climate for growing coffee beans. This means that all coffee beans are imported from other countries. Some oil is produced in the United States, but it is still necessary to import 40 to 50 percent of the needed oil. Cameras, bananas, tea, and shoes are brought in for sale in large amounts. Many foreign cars are for sale in the United States, such as Toyota, Honda, and Mercedes.

What Is International Trade?

American enjoyment of these imported goods is the result of **international trade**, or trade among nations. Countries may buy some products from other nations, but they also sell products to other countries. Most countries trade because they cannot produce all the products that they need. Countries specialize in the products that they can make the best with the natural, land, and labor resources they have. For example, the United States has rich farmland, a highly skilled work force, and advanced technology. Therefore, the United States sells many types of food, machines, tools, aircraft, and office equipment to other countries. American airplanes are used by many foreign airline companies.

A. Use the information above to complete each sentence correctly.

1. The United States does not have the right climate for _____ coffee beans.

2. Many foreign airline companies use American _____ .

3. Much oil is _____ by the United States.

4. The United States has a highly _____ work force.

5. International _____ is selling among countries.

6. Many _____ cars are for sale in the United States.

7. The United States has rich _____ .

8. The United States sells _____ , machines, tools, and other items to foreign countries.

The Government Has Some Control Over Trade

Although most international trade in America is carried on by private business, the government does make rules and laws for this trade. American workers and products must be protected. If too many foreign goods are sold in America, some American businesses could not survive. **Tariffs** and **quotas** are the two main ways in which the government controls trade.

A tariff is a tax placed on an imported product to raise its price. Tariffs are usually imposed if a foreign product can be sold much cheaper than a similar American product. For example, if a Japanese radio can be sold cheaper than American radios for sale in this country, then the government would place a tariff on the radio. This tax would bring the price of the Japanese radio closer to other radios. The government also uses tariffs to discourage foreign countries from selling their products in the United States. If the American government wants other countries to bring products into the United States, tariffs are lowered.

A quota is a limit placed on the amount of a foreign product that can be sold in the United States. The government sets quotas on certain products. Usually a quota is set because a tariff did not raise the price high enough. Too many foreign products with low prices could hurt American producers.

Some Products Are Completely Banned in the United States

The government has also found it necessary to prevent some foreign products from being sold at all in the United States. Ivory and some furs are banned because these products require the killing of endangered or rare animals. Safety is another important reason for banning goods. Certain food products, fresh fruits and dairy items, are not allowed for health reasons. If a foreign automobile does not meet American safety standards, then it cannot be sold in the United States.

How Much Free Trade Should the United States Take Part in?

Many arguments for and against free trade have existed throughout American history. Such arguments have been especially true about imported goods. Some people feel that there should be no government control of trade. They believe that any country should be allowed to sell its products in this country. Other people think that some goods should be completely banned or at least under the strict control of the government. These people who are against free trade feel that imported goods keep American goods from being sold. Such imports might put American workers out of work. People against free trade are known as **protectionists.** They favor methods such as tariffs and quotas, which discourage free trade.

Why Are Protectionists Against Free Trade?

National defense is the main reason protectionists give for limiting free trade. The United States might become too dependent on foreign countries for products such as food, oil, and weapons. In time of war, the United States might not be able to get these supplies. Protectionists believe Americans must be independent to be safe. Another reason for limiting free trade is to prevent jobs and money from being taken away from American businesses and workers.

Why Do Some People Favor Free Trade?

Those who favor free trade agree that it causes some problems for American business. However, free trade among nations also has many benefits.

First, if countries are stopped from selling their products in the United States, American goods will not be allowed into their countries. American businesses need to sell products on a worldwide market. Second, free trade gives consumers a large selection of goods at low prices. Finally, strong and active trading among nations makes them friendlier to each other and reduces the chances of war.

B. Match the terms on the left with the phrases on the right.

_____ 1. protectionists

_____ 2. tariffs

_____ 3. quotas

_____ 4. ivory and some furs

_____ 5. national defense

_____ 6. wars

_____ 7. free trade

a. are completely banned in the United States

b. might be reduced by strong and active international trade

c. no interference from the government in international trade

d. favor tariffs and quotas

e. are limits placed on the amounts of products that can be sold

f. are taxes placed on imported goods

g. is the most important reason for limiting free trade

Review Unit 5

A. Complete the exercise.

1. Name two laws that were passed by the government to control unfair business practices.

   _____

2. Name two agencies that were set up to further control business.

   _____

3. Which agency was set up by the government to control the handling of food and prescription drugs? _____

4. Which act was passed by the government to provide workers with retirement benefits?

   _____

5. Name three goods and services provided by the

   a. federal government _____

   b. state and local governments _____

6. Name two things the government does to control international trade.

   _____

7. Name two products the United States imports from other countries.

   _____

8. Name two products the United States sells to other countries.

   _____

9. Why do protectionists want strong government control of trade?

   _____

   _____

10. Why do some people favor free trade among nations?

    _____

    _____

Jobs in the Free Enterprise System

What Kinds of Jobs Can People Choose?

People may earn money from many types of jobs. High school students may hold a part-time job. The type of work people do depends on their abilities and skills. As people's skills increase, their choice of jobs will also increase. Some people may choose full-time employment after high school. Others may decide to go on to college or to another type of school. Sooner or later, everyone will be a full-time member of the workforce. The skills people have will be valuable to an employer and will help earn an income. Most people will probably earn an income by doing one of the following types of work.

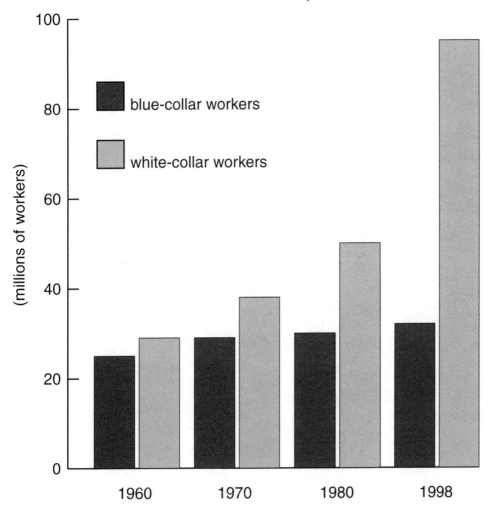

TRENDS IN WORKFORCE, 1960–1998

Main Types of Workers

1. White-collar workers—office workers, teachers, secretaries, insurance agents

2. Blue-collar workers—factory workers, outdoor workers, carpenters, plumbers

3. Service workers—barbers, janitors, police officers, and others who provide services

4. Farm workers—farm owners and people who work on farms

The demand for white-collar workers has grown. Many former blue-collar workers are going to college to learn things, such as computing and business skills.

How Is Money Paid to Workers?

The money people receive for work is paid as an **hourly wage** or as a salary. An hourly wage is usually paid per hour of work. Salaries are earnings paid for a period of time, such as a week, month, or year. Some people, such as salespeople and agents, also earn **commissions**. These people are given an actual percentage of the money received from sales they make. **Tips** and **bonuses** are extra money earned by some workers in addition to their wages or salaries. A tip is money usually paid by a customer to a worker. Tips make up part of the income of restaurant servers, messengers, and delivery people. A bonus is money paid to an employee in addition to salary. It is paid by an employer to a worker for a special reason or on a special occasion. For example, many businesses give holiday bonuses to their employees.

A. Choose the word that correctly completes each of the following sentences. Write the words on the lines provided.

1. When people work, the _____ a person has will decide what type of job the person holds. (income, skills and abilities)

2. Carpenters and plumbers are considered _____ workers. (white-collar, blue-collar)

3. Teachers and office workers are considered _____ workers. (white-collar, blue-collar)

4. A commission is often paid to _____ . (servers, salespeople)

5. _____ are paid to certain workers by customers. (Tips, Bonuses)

6. Some companies pay _____ to workers for special reasons. (tips, bonuses)

7. Two main types of incomes are _____ and _____ . (tip, bonus, hourly wage, commission, salary)

8. According to the graph on page 71, the demand for _____ workers has grown. (white-collar, blue-collar)

9. The graph also shows that in _____ , there were 20 million more white-collar workers than blue-collar workers. (1970, 1980, 1998)

Benefits to Consider When Choosing a Job

Although income will be important when choosing a job, there are other things to consider. Many companies offer workers **benefits** in addition to salaries or wages. Benefits are not given as money but as indirect payments. Some of the most common types of benefits are paid vacations, paid sick days, paid holidays, health and life insurance plans, and retirement plans.

Many companies offer special benefits to attract employees. Salespeople often receive the free use of a company car and have their meals paid for during work hours. To help employees who have children, some companies provide day-care centers. **Flextime,** or work hours and schedules that can be adjusted, may also be offered by some businesses. Flextime helps parents who must consider the care of their small children when they accept jobs.

Workers Have Rights in a Free Enterprise System

All workers have certain rights that are protected by law. Unit 5 stated some ways in which the government protects workers. Employers must follow laws concerning income security, minimum wage, safety and health on the job, and retirement payments. Two important laws concern **unemployment compensation** and **workers' compensation.** Workers' compensation is money paid to workers who have been injured or who have become sick because of their job. They receive an income until they are well enough to return to work. Unemployment compensation is money paid to workers who do not willingly leave their jobs but who are let go by their employers. Such payments are given for a set period of time. They help people to pay their bills while they search for a new job.

In addition to the rights guaranteed by law, there are other things that workers can ask for. If someone works overtime, in some jobs, that person should receive additional pay. Workers also have the right to ask for a raise if they feel they deserve it. However, employers have the right to turn employees down.

Help for the Jobless

One of the many tasks of the Department of Labor is to keep track of the number of people in the United States who are jobless. The department publishes reports on employment opportunities, listing the industries and companies that they think will need new employees. How do these reports help the jobless? For example, if the department reports that the service industry (health care, education, and hospital workers) will show an increase, citizens may choose to look for jobs in this industry.

Here are some trends in labor that the department forsees through 2006:

• workers ages 16–24 will increase by 3 million
• health care will see the largest increase in jobs for any industry
• computer related jobs will grow rapidly
• two out of three job openings will require on-the-job training

People also have the right to ask for a **promotion,** which is a better job in the business where someone is employed. An employer may not know that an employee wants a better job unless the employee asks. Employees may have to prove that they are qualified. If a company does not have many chances for promotions, then employees have the right to look for another job. Most employers are aware that good workers wish to keep getting better jobs in order to earn more money. If necessary, they will keep changing jobs. In the past, most workers changed jobs about every twenty years, if at all. Now, most workers change jobs about every five years.

B. **Read the definitions listed in the box below. Choose the definition that will match each of the italicized phrases in the following sentences. Write the definition on the lines provided.**

• money paid to workers who are injured or become sick because of their job   • indirect payments to workers, such as paid vacations and holidays
• money paid to workers who have been let go by their employers   • a better job in the business where a person works

1. Workers at most companies are able to receive *workers' compensation.*

    _____

    _____

2. A worker should consider *benefits* when looking for a job.

    _____

    _____

3. A worker has the right to ask for a *promotion.*

    _____

    _____

4. Most workers are entitled to *unemployment compensation,* if needed.

    _____

    _____

Using Income Wisely

Consumers Should Plan Ahead

In a free enterprise system, consumers are allowed to act in their own self-interest. They may use their money to buy anything they want from any business they choose. There are thousands of goods and services for sale. How can consumers be sure they are using their money wisely? In the following sections are some suggestions to help consumers spend their money wisely.

Consumers Can Plan Spending by Making a Budget

Consumers have a limited amount of money to spend. One way to decide which products and services to buy is to make a written plan for spending. This is called a budget. **Expenses** are all the items people spend money on. By carefully writing down expenses, consumers will know how much money they will have left. They can save some money for emergencies and for the extra things that they would like to have. First, a budget should show the amount of money coming in. Then, it should have a listing of expenses and savings. The following pie graph shows how money might be spent. Everyone should try to save a part of his or her income. One suggested amount is about 25 percent, or 25¢ out of every $1.00. This much should be saved if sharing expenses or if living at home. If living alone, then 10 percent is the suggested amount.

A. **Look at the percents on the pie graph below. The monthly salary is $900. Figure the amount in dollars that would be spent in each of the following areas. The first one has been done for you.**

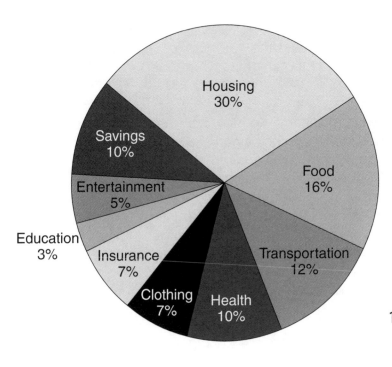

1. Housing (30%) . . . . __$270__
   ($900 x 0.30 = $270)

2. Food (16%) . . . . _____

3. Transportation (12%) . . . . . _____

4. Health (10%) . . . . _____

5. Clothing (7%) . . . . _____

6. Insurance (7%) . . . . _____

7. Education (3%) . . . . _____

8. Entertainment (5%) . . . . . . _____

9. Savings (10%) . . . . _____

10. TOTAL . . . . _____

Expenses plus savings should equal a person's entire monthly income. When living alone, people have many expenses. As the graph on page 75 shows, the most money will be spent on food and housing. For people not living alone, expenses will be less. They might include such things as gasoline (for a car), clothing, recreation, and savings.

The amounts in a budget can be changed to fit individual needs. When one item on a budget is changed, at least one of the others must be changed. If housing is increased to 35 percent of the $900 (900 x 0.35 = $315), then some other part of the budget will have to be reduced. Less money might be spent on entertainment or food. A person may have to eat in restaurants less often or make fewer trips to the movies.

Housing and food will take the largest part of the budget. When living alone, a person will probably have to pay for housing. A person might pay rent for a room or an apartment. Others might live alone or share the rent by living with friends. Food will also take up a large part of a budget, whether eating out or at home. Here are three important things to consider before shopping for food:

1. Make a list and plan meals in order to shop as seldom as possible during a pay period.

2. Shop for products on sale. Compare brands to make the best buy.

3. Do not buy on "impulse." Buy only the items on the list.

Check Products and Services Thoroughly Before Buying

Wise consumers budget their money. They also learn about the quality, price, and warranties of products and services before purchasing anything. Consumers should be sure to do the following:

First, check the quality. Personal experience will provide an important source of information about products and services. Those who have had a bad experience with a product will not buy it again. For example, owning a certain make of car will help to decide whether to buy that make of car again. The experiences of others are also good sources of product information. Advertising is the most common way people learn about products. Television and newspapers contain many advertisements. Although government laws control truth in advertising and false claims, ads for products can leave out certain information. To get good information, read a consumer magazine, such as *Consumer Reports*. It can tell about the safety and quality of many products and how long they should last.

Second, check the price. One way to be sure to get the best price is to comparison shop. **Comparison shopping** means comparing the price of items in several different stores. Being aware of sales is another way to find the best price. In sales, a store reduces the prices of products to attract customers and to sell these products quickly. Sales are usually announced in advance. For example, the store may put a sign in the window.

Unit pricing is another special form of comparison shopping. Unit pricing tells how much each item costs in a certain amount. This amount may be a quart or a gallon, a foot or a yard, or another measure. Products for which unit prices are shown may include milk or gas, ribbon or cloth.

Finally, check for a **warranty.** A warranty is a promise made by the maker or the seller of a product. This promise may be either written or unwritten. A written warranty states that the product is in good working condition. The length of time the written warranty is in effect may run from several months to a year, depending on the product. The warranty states that if there is a problem, it will be taken care of. If a product does not have a written warranty, the customer still has certain rights. Any product should do what it is supposed to do.

Even if the promise is not in writing, a consumer should be able to return a product that does not live up to the promises of the producer. Reliable stores will make every effort to keep their customers happy. They will exchange, repair, or give refunds for faulty products.

B. **Listed below are terms taken from the lesson. Write a sentence to explain what each of these words or phrases means.**

1. Comparison shopping _____

    _____

2. Sale _____

    _____

3. Unit pricing _____

    _____

4. Impulse buying _____

    _____

5. Warranty _____

    _____

6. *Consumer Reports* _____

    _____

Method of Payment: Cash or Credit

After checking the product or service and making a purchase, another decision has to be made. How will people pay for their purchases? Two main choices are cash and **credit.** Many people pay for purchases with cash, or bills and coins. Cash is convenient and is accepted everywhere. When living alone, people are likely to buy things on credit and use cash as well.

Credit means making the purchase now, but paying for it later. The most common types of credit, or charge accounts, include store charge accounts, bank credit cards (Visa and Master Card), and gasoline credit cards. Private credit cards, which are often used for travel and entertainment, include American Express and Diners Club.

There are two main types of credit. The first type is **regular credit.** The entire bill must be paid in full at the end of a certain time period, usually thirty days. American Express is an example of regular credit, which must be paid in full each month.

The second type is **revolving credit.** Part of the bill must be paid each month, and the rest of the money owed is carried over for later payments. Most store charge accounts and bank credit cards are revolving credit accounts. These revolving accounts charge a fee, known as a **finance charge,** for the right to "buy now and pay later." This finance charge is a percentage of the money owed and is added to the bill.

Some credit card companies charge an **annual fee.** This is a fee that the person using the card must pay each year for the right to use it. Both regular credit and revolving credit cards may have an annual fee. Not all credit card companies charge this fee.

Sometimes credit is better than cash. Certain expenses, such as travel expenses, are easier and safer to pay for with credit. Consumers can avoid carrying large amounts of cash that might be lost or stolen. Certain services, such as car repairs, can also be paid for with credit.

Consumers can choose to pay for business travel and meals by using a credit card.

C. **Read the words listed in the box below. Choose the word that correctly completes each of the following sentences. Write the words on the lines provided.**

Revolving	Credit	American Express
Traveling	Regular	Visa

1. _____ means that someone can buy something now and pay for it later.

2. _____ credit means the bill must be paid in full at the end of a certain period of time.

3. _____ credit accounts require that only part of the bill be paid each month.

4. _____ is an example of a regular credit account.

5. _____ expenses are easier and safer to pay for with credit.

6. _____ is an example of a revolving credit account.

Spending Money

Consumers spend their money on many products that are used right away and must be replaced. Some examples include food, gasoline, medicines, and cosmetics. These items are not expensive. Many consumers use a trial and error system when buying them. In other words, they try these products. If they are not satisfied with the products after using them, they will not buy them again.

Other goods are more expensive and last a longer period of time. Wise consumers do not use the trial and error system to buy them. Such items are referred to as **durable goods.** These products are bought only once in a long period of time. Examples of durable goods are cars, televisions, appliances, or furniture. These items are usually expensive. When shopping for durable goods, consumers should spend more time comparing and checking prices in the stores where these items can be bought. In this way, consumers can save money.

Buying a Used Car

A car is one durable good that most consumers buy at some time. Many times this is a used car. Here are some items consumers should consider when deciding to buy a used car.

- **Check the budget**
  Consumers must decide whether they have all the money they need or whether they need to borrow money. After comparing the prices of cars, a person might decide to save for a while rather than borrow. If a person decides to borrow, that person must decide whether to borrow from family, friends, or a bank.

- **Study the car market**
  When deciding how much money to invest in a car, consumers should read the newspaper car ads, or ads found on the Internet. They must choose a car within the right price range. Then they can go to the library or research on the Internet to read about prices and repair records in a consumer book and write down all this information.

- **Shop around before buying**
  Consumers should test drive some cars they read about in ads. They should also check the mileage, and ask the owner questions about repairs that have been made. Before buying the car, the buyer should take it to a good mechanic. The money paid to the mechanic may save the buyer from buying a faulty car. Next, the buyer should see if the price the owner is asking is the same as the prices found when researching. If the buyer decides to buy a car, that person should think about it overnight before making a final decision.

Saving Money in a Bank

The most common way to save money is to deposit it in a bank for future use. That money will also earn interest when it is placed in a bank. Many people use a **passbook savings account.** Each deposit is recorded in a small booklet, the **passbook.** After a certain amount of time, interest is added to the amount saved. To take money out from the account, a person brings the book to the bank and requests a certain amount of money. This amount is then subtracted from the amount of savings.

Another way to save money in a bank is through a **Certificate of Deposit (CD).** This certificate usually requires a minimum deposit, around $500 or $1,000. Money is deposited for a certain period of time, ranging from three months to seven years, at a special rate of interest. The money in the CD cannot be taken out too early, or the interest will not be paid. A two-year CD might earn 8.5 percent interest, but a five-year CD might earn 9.5 percent.

Investing in Common Stock Is Another Way of Saving Money

Common stocks are small shares of corporations that are bought by people who hope to make money. Corporations sell common stocks to raise money. The people who buy the stocks are called stockholders. If the corporation does well, the value of these stocks increases. Then, a stockholder might decide to sell the stock. The stockholders are also paid money, called dividends, about every three months. Buying stock is not as safe as depositing money in a savings account. Stocks can decrease, as well as increase, in value.

Stock exchanges are places where the buying and selling of stock is handled. They keep track of the daily changing prices of the thousands of stocks for sale. A **stockbroker** is someone who is paid to help other people buy and sell stock. The buyers and sellers may never actually meet. The cost of buying and selling stock for the investor depends on the price and number of shares bought or sold.

NEW YORK STOCK EXCHANGE ISSUES CONSOLIDATE

Stockholders and stockbrokers can follow the prices of stocks in the newspaper.

A. Complete the exercise.

1. List three examples of durable goods.

   a. _____ b. _____ c. _____

2. List three products consumers buy that are not durable goods and that must be replaced often.

   a. _____ b. _____ c. _____

3. What should consumers do concerning the price of a durable good they wish to buy?

   _____

4. What is the most common way consumers can save their money?

   _____

5. What are small shares of corporations that are bought by people trying to make money?

   _____

6. Why is buying stocks not as safe as depositing money in a bank?

   _____

   _____

7. What is a dividend?

   _____

   _____

Borrowing Money Is Often Necessary for Consumers

Most consumers borrow large sums of money at certain times. The last lesson discussed credit and credit accounts as a way of borrowing small amounts of money for inexpensive purchases. It is not always possible to use credit or even to save for more expensive items. Sometimes people need items such as cars or refrigerators right away. People who have steady incomes can borrow in several ways. For example, a family with a steady income can buy a home by taking a **mortgage loan.** Saving enough money for a home would take years. There are two common ways to borrow money.

Mortgage Loans

A mortgage loan is usually made by the **lender** (bank or other financial institution) for the purchase of a house, land, or other type of building. Mortgage loans are given to people who have a certain amount of regular income. A mortgage loan is repaid in monthly payments for a period of ten to thirty years. Suppose a family is applying for a mortgage loan to buy a house worth $70,000. The family has saved $10,000 for a **down payment,** or the part of the cost paid right away. The bank will lend them $60,000. The interest rate is figured out, and a monthly payment is decided on. The amount paid back will be the $60,000 plus the interest. The family signs a written promise to make payments every month for a certain number of years until the loan is repaid. The family also agrees to give the bank a **mortgage** against the property, in this case the house. A mortgage is a legal paper that says the bank owns the house until the loan is repaid. If the payments are not made, the bank can take the house from the family and resell it.

Installment Loans

Consumers might use an **installment loan** to buy such things as cars, televisions, appliances, boats, or motorcycles. The interest on the money borrowed is included in the loan. The borrower must pay back this total amount in **installments,** or regular payments, over a period of time, usually from one to five years. Just as with a mortgage loan, a down payment is required. A consumer can use the product while making the loan payments. Some lenders ask borrowers to give **collateral,** such as property or stocks, to be certain that the loan will be repaid. If the person borrowing money does not repay the loan, then the property will be taken by the lender to pay the debt.

B. Match the terms on the left with the definitions on the right.

_____ 1. installments   a. regular payments made over a period of time
_____ 2. collateral   b. property given to assure loan payment
_____ 3. installment loan   c. the part of the cost paid right away
_____ 4. down payment   d. loan used to buy a car
_____ 5. mortgage loan   e. loan used to buy a house

Taxation Lesson 4

Governments Receive Their Money From Taxes

The last unit discussed how governments spend money to provide people with certain services. These services include roads, schools, post offices, and courts. Citizens pay for these services when they pay taxes. A tax is a required payment. Americans do not have a choice about paying taxes. They pay taxes on income to both the federal and state governments. Also, Americans usually pay taxes when buying goods and services. Americans also pay "hidden" taxes. For example, the price of a gallon of gasoline includes both federal and state taxes.

Income Tax Makes Up 57 Percent of the Federal Government's Income

Income tax is a percentage of a person's or a corporation's income that is paid to the government every year. The income tax is the simplest tax to collect. Employers **withhold,** or keep back, a certain amount from a worker's paycheck. In the case of the federal tax, this money is sent to the federal government's Internal Revenue Service (IRS).

On or before April 15 of each year, people earning over a certain amount of money must fill out their income tax form and send it to the IRS. The form tells the government how much income a person earned throughout the year and how much tax is owed. The amount of tax already sent to the IRS is subtracted from the total amount owed. This tells the amount that still has to be paid. Sometimes people do not have to pay more tax because enough, or even too much, was withheld from their income that year. If too much was withheld, they will get money back from the IRS in the form of a refund check.

Taxable Income Is the Money Left After Deductions and Exemptions

Not all of a person's income is taxed. A person's taxable income is not the same as a person's total income. When figuring out taxable income, a person can subtract or deduct certain expenses. These **deductions** include mortgage interest payments, money given to charities, and medical bills over a certain percentage. A person is also allowed **exemptions,** which are amounts of money subtracted from the total income. Exemptions are allowed for every person in the taxpayer's family. Additional exemptions are allowed if the taxpayer is over 65 and/or blind.

Social Security Tax

The **Social Security tax** began in 1935 when Congress passed the Social Security Act. This tax provides income for the elderly and other persons who are unable to earn an income. The money paid into Social Security is taken out of people's paychecks before they receive it. The money goes into a special fund. The employer puts in the same amount as the worker. The federal government uses the fund to pay workers an income each month after they retire. Social Security is also used to support widows, widowers, and children.

Kinds of Taxes

The **sales tax** is the main tax collected by the states. These taxes are paid when goods or services are bought. The rates differ from state to state. The amount of sales tax by state is shown on the map below. They range from 3 percent to 8 percent of the selling price of the purchase. In some states, food, clothing, medicine, and certain services are free from tax. Forty-five states have a sales tax.

An **excise tax** is paid on certain goods or services. It is part of the cost of the item and is included in the price. Both federal and state governments use excise taxes on such things as alcoholic beverages, tobacco, gasoline, tires, movies, and airline tickets.

Local governments depend on **property tax,** or tax on private property, for most of the money they need. Most of the money collected in property taxes is used for public schools. A property tax is set according to the **assessed value,** which is only part of the full value, of such property as land, buildings, or vehicles. Each community will set a tax rate that depends on the amount of money it needs to provide services for its residents. This amount is called a **tax base.** Sometimes, property is taxed on its full value. More often, an assessed value is used. For example, a house that could be sold for $75,000 might be assessed at 20 percent of its market value. ($75,000 x 0.20 = $15,000.) If the tax rate of a community is 2 percent on the assessed value of this house, the community would receive $300 in taxes. ($15,000 x 0.02 = $300.)

SALES TAX BY STATE

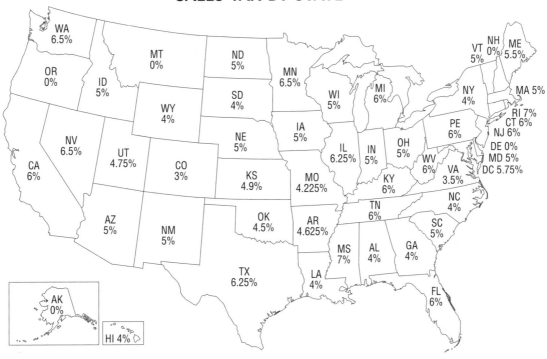

Taxpayers Should Be Aware of How Their Tax Money Is Spent
The law says that citizens must pay any taxes they owe to federal, state, and local governments. Citizens should be aware of how their tax dollars are being used. For example, taxpayers should notice whether highways and roads are being kept in good repair, and whether recreation areas are well kept. If there are areas of government spending that could be improved, such as education, taxpayers should let their elected officials know. They can write letters directly to local officials or members of the state congress. Writing a letter to the editor of a local newspaper is another way to get the attention of officials. Most elected officials are interested in how the voters of their communities feel about the way their communities are run.

A. **Choose the word that correctly completes each of the following sentences. Write the words on the lines provided.**

1. Americans do not have a choice about paying _____ .
    (income, taxes, refunds)

2. The _____ is a part of a person's income that is paid to the government each year. (hidden tax, exemption tax, income tax)

3. _____ income is the part of income that is taxed.
    (Withholding, Taxable, Monthly)

4. A _____ is the part of income that is not taxed. It includes such expenses as money paid for mortgage and medical bills.
    (deduction, payment, hidden tax)

5. _____ is the amount of money subtracted from a person's total income for the number of family members. (A deduction, An exemption)

B. **Write the letter of the correct type of tax for each of the following statements.**

a. sales tax	b. excise tax	c. Social Security tax	d. property tax

_____ **1.** began in 1935
_____ **2.** used for education
_____ **3.** supports widows or widowers
_____ **4.** different rates for each state
_____ **5.** set on assessed value
_____ **6.** income for elderly
_____ **7.** paid on gasoline
_____ **8.** medicine may be exempt

Review Unit 6

A. **Read the phrases listed in the box below. Choose the phrase that correctly completes each sentence. Write the phrase on the lines provided.**

• "buy now, pay later"   • paid vacations and health insurance
• paid to workers let go by their employers   • in 45 states
• require a minimum deposit   • income to retired people
• paid for job-related injuries   • paid only by people who own land or buildings
• paid by all Americans   • mortgage loan
• a product will work the way it should
• small shares of corporations

1. Taxes are _____ .

2. Common stocks are _____ .

3. Certificates of Deposit usually _____ .

4. Workers' compensation is _____ .

5. A written warranty assures a consumer that _____ .

6. Unemployment compensation is _____ .

7. Credit means _____ .

8. Property tax is _____ .

9. Borrowing for a home is done with a _____ .

10. Benefits for employees may include _____ .

11. Social Security tax is used to pay _____ .

12. A sales tax is used _____ .

This book has dealt with the free enterprise system—**capitalism**—of economics used in the United States. This system is only one of three economic systems used by countries in the world today. Two other systems are **communism** and **socialism.** Countries are said to operate under one of these three economic systems.

In socialism, the government owns some property and manages production of some goods and services. Sweden's socialist government manages all the major industries. It also has great control over human services, such as health care, education, care of the elderly, and other welfare services. In order to do this, Sweden's government depends on tax money. Therefore, the tax rate is extremely high.

Communism is an economic and government system in which there is no private property. The state owns everything. The former Soviet Union was once a communist nation. However, the communist government ended there in 1991. Currently, China is the largest communist nation in the world.

Each of these systems needs and uses various resources to produce goods and services for its citizens. Natural resources like trees, oil, water, and farmland are found in nature. Human resources involve the work that people do. This labor can be mental or physical.

Capital includes money and the things bought with it: factories, machines, highways, bridges, shipyards, trucks, and trains. Each major economic system controls and uses its resources in different ways. The chart below explains how these resources are handled in the three major economic systems.

	CAPITALISM	SOCIALISM	COMMUNISM
Who own the resources?	Resources are privately owned and run.	Some basic resources are government owned and run. Others are privately owned.	Resources are owned and run by the government.
How are the resources given out?	Businesses obtain their own resources so that they can earn profits.	The government decides how to give resources to major businesses.	The government plans the use of all resources.
What is the government's role?	The government has limited involvement in how businesses are operated.	Major businesses are controlled by the government.	The government controls all businesses.

End-of-Book Test

A. Write *True* or *False* on the line before each statement.

_____ 1. Economics is the study of how people's needs and wants are taken care of by their own efforts to earn a living.

_____ 2. The market price is the price that businesses set for a good or service.

_____ 3. A sole proprietorship is a business owned by two or more people.

_____ 4. Demand is the amount of a product that is offered for sale, and supply is the amount of a product that consumers want to buy.

_____ 5. Economic growth is the increase in the amount of goods and services produced in a country.

_____ 6. A recession is a more serious economic problem than a depression.

_____ 7. The United States government cannot make laws that affect business.

_____ 8. Workers have certain rights that are protected by law in a free enterprise system.

_____ 9. The two main functions of banks are to offer credit cards and enforce banking laws.

_____ 10. The American free enterprise system developed in the American colonies as a result of British mercantilism.

B. Use the terms in the box to complete the following sentences correctly. Write the terms on the lines.

budget	corporation	inflation	monopoly	tariff
consumer	credit	market	profit	wage

1. Purchasing something now and paying for it later is called _____ .

2. Control of the production of goods and services by one business is a _____ .

3. _____ takes place when prices rise quickly, but incomes do not rise as fast.

4. A _____ is a plan that tells how money will be spent.

5. The amount of money left in a business after all the costs of production have been paid is _____ .

6. A _____ is someone who buys and uses goods or services.

7. Money paid per hour of work is a _____ .

8. A _____ is a tax placed on an imported product to raise its price.

9. A business owned by more than one person is called a _____ .

10. A _____ is anywhere buying and selling takes place.

C. Write the letter of the correct answer to each question on the line.

_____ 1. What is the central banking system in the United States?

     a. Federal Reserve System   **c.** Federal Trade Commission
     b. Food and Drug Administration   **d.** Securities and Exchange Commission

_____ 2. What word means the study of how people's needs and wants are taken care of by their own efforts to earn a living?

     a. competition   **c.** labor
     b. economics   **d.** consumer

_____ 3. What term is used to refer to risking only part of one's investments in a business?

     a. unlimited liability   **c.** measure of value
     b. installment   **d.** limited liability

_____ 4. What is money paid by a customer to a worker called?

     a. commission   **c.** bonus
     b. salary   **d.** tip

_____ 5. What is another name for bills and coins?

     a. credit   **c.** cash
     b. checks   **d.** promissory note

D. Match the words in the first column with the meanings in the second column. Write the letter of the correct meaning on the line.

_____ 1. deposit   **a.** one who owns and operates his or her own business
_____ 2. collateral   **b.** yearly percentage of income paid to the government
_____ 3. entrepreneur   **c.** limit placed on the amount of a foreign product that
_____ 4. rent   can be sold in the United States
_____ 5. workers' compensation   **d.** money paid to workers injured on the job
_____ 6. unemployment   **e.** regular payment to pay off a loan
_____ 7. income tax   **f.** place where stocks are sold and bought
_____ 8. quota   **g.** money placed into a bank
_____ 9. installment   **h.** out of work
_____ 10. stock market   **i.** money paid for the use of someone else's property
     j. something of value used to make sure a loan will be repaid

E. Answer the following questions with complete sentences.

1. What is the main role of consumers?

   _____

   _____

   _____

2. How does trial and error work?

   _____

   _____

   _____

3. What are two ways the government affects business in a free enterprise system?

   _____

   _____

   _____

4. What are the four main types of workers in the American workforce?

   _____

   _____

   _____

5. What are the three main economic systems in the world? Which one is used in the United States?

   _____

   _____

   _____

Glossary

A

agriculture: Farming; having to do with raising crops or animals for food or profit. (8)

annual fee: A fee credit card users must pay each year for the right to use it. (78)

assessed value: Part of the full value of land, buildings, or vehicles. (85)

B

bartering: The act of trading something for something else. (50)

benefits: Indirect payments to workers, such as vacations, sick days, holidays, insurance and retirement plans. (73)

blacklisted: Placing union workers on a list so that other employers will not hire them. (40)

bonus: Money paid in addition to salary for a special reason or occasion. (72)

budget: A written plan that tells how much money is available and how it is spent. (65)

business cycle: The series of changes in the American economy from one period of prosperity to the next. (46)

C

capital: Money and the things bought with it. (14)

capitalism: The free enterprise system of economics. (88)

cash: Currency that includes bills or coins. (56)

Certificate of Deposit (CD): Certificate that represents a deposit of money for a certain period of time; the deposit gains interest. (81)

charter: A document a state government gives to a business to make the business a legal corporation. (34)

check: Currency used in place of cash that orders a bank to pay money from one person's account to another person or business. (50)

clinic: A small medical facility used to treat or diagnose illness. (65)

collateral: Something of value, such as property or stocks, used to make sure that a loan will be repaid. (83)

collective bargaining: A meeting between a labor union and an employer to reach an agreement on issues. (40)

commission: Money that some workers, such as agents or salespeople, earn that is a percentage of the money received from sales. (72)

common stocks: Small shares of corporations bought to make money. (81)

communism: An economic and government system in which there is no private property; the state owns everything. (88)

comparison shopping: Comparing the price of items in several different stores. (77)

competition: The rivalry among businesses for the consumer's money. (24)

consumer: An individual who uses goods and services. (5)

Consumer Price Index (CPI): A measure of the change in price of about 400 consumer goods and services from year to year. (49)

contract: A legal document that sets up rules for two or more parties to follow. (34)

corporation: A large business owned by more than one person. (32)

craft guild: A group that represented skilled workers and trained others in the trade. (9)

credit: Making a purchase now and paying for it later. (78)

credit card: A card used to buy something on credit and pay for the purchase later. (50)

currency: Coins and paper money (cash or checks) consumers use to buy things. (50)

D

debt interest: Interest owed on a loan. (65)

deduction: The part of income that is not taxed, such as mortgage payments or medical bills over a certain percentage. (84)

demand: The amount of a product that consumers want to buy. (20)

demand deposit: A deposit placed into a checking account that can be taken out at any time. (51)

deposit: Money placed into a bank for safekeeping and convenience. (51)

depression: A great slowdown in the economy. (46)

dividend: A payment made to a stockholder by a business. (28)

domestic system: A kind of business system in which workers produce goods in their homes. (9)

down payment: Part of the cost of something expensive that is paid right away. (83)

durable goods: Expensive goods that last a long period of time, and are bought only once in a while. (80)

E

economic growth: The increase in the amount of goods and services produced in a country. (43)

economics: The study of how people's needs and wants are taken care of by their own efforts to earn a living, and the study of how countries use resources to provide goods and services. (5)

efficiency: The state businesses can achieve when they manage time and use workers well. (25)

employment: The act of holding a job to make a living. (63)

entrepreneur: A person who owns, operates, and earns an income from his or her own business. (5)

excise tax: Tax on certain goods or services, such as alcoholic beverages and airline tickets, that is included in the cost of the item. (85)

exemption: Amounts of money subtracted from a person's total income for every person in the taxpayers' family, or if the taxpayer is over 65 and/or blind. (84)

expenses: Items people spend money on. (75)

F

factory system: A kind of business system in which goods are produced in owned or rented buildings. (9)

Federal Reserve System: The central banking system of the United States that offers services to its member banks and controls the supply of money. (53)

feudalism: A system in which a feudal lord gave protection to the people who lived and worked on his land in return for loyalty. (8)

fief: The land owned by a lord in feudalism. (8)

finance charge: A fee charged to a person using a revolving credit account. (78)

fiscal year: A twelve-month period of financial planning. (65)

flextime: Work hours and schedules that can be adjusted. (73)

free enterprise system: A system in which the individual can make many choices, such as deciding what to buy or what type of job to look for. (5)

G

goods and services: Items such as natural resources, or things people do for one another such as police protection, that are used to take care of the wishes of citizens. (5)

Great Depression: A huge economic slowdown in the 1930s and 1940s that caused high unemployment and bank failures. (45)

Gross National Product (GNP): The total yearly dollar value of all goods and services used to measure the growth of the American economy. (44)

guild: A group of workers with similar interests. (9)

H

hourly wage: Money paid per hour of work. (72)

I

income: Money earned. (16)

income security: Money paid to the federal government that is used to protect people's incomes. (63)

income tax: A percentage of a person's income that is paid to the government every year. (84)

inflation: Increase in prices that is more rapid than the increase in people's incomes. (48)

installment: Regular payments made over a period of time to pay off a loan. (83)

installment loan: A loan consumers use to buy such things as vehicles or appliances. (83)

interest: Money paid to an individual who lends money to others. (28)

international trade: Trade among nations. (67)

investment: An arrangement that is intended to earn more money. (28)

L

labor: The work people do. (12)

labor force: The workforce. (5)

labor union: Group of workers whose main purpose is to protect their own economic interest. (39)

lender: A bank or other financial company that lends money. (83)

limited liability: Risking only part of one's investment in a business. (35)

loan: Money borrowed. (51)

M

market: Anywhere buying and selling takes place. (18)

market price: A price that most consumers will pay for a good or service. (21)

material goods: Things that can be used or consumed, such as food and clothing. (5)

measure of value: Something that shows the worth of goods or services. (50)

medium of exchange: Something that all people recognize as a means of buying goods or services. (50)

mental: Thinking; relating to the mind. (11)

mercantilism: An economic system based on the idea that a country becomes strong by having wealth and strict government and market control. (9)

merchant's guild: A guild that regulated weights and measures as well as the types and prices of goods to be sold. (9)

merger: When one company buys another and the two become one firm. (58)

minimum wage: The lowest amount a worker can be paid. (61)

money: Something accepted as a medium of exchange, measure of value, or payment. (5)

monopoly: Control of the production of goods or services by one business. (57)

mortgage: A legal paper issued when buying a house that says the bank owns the house until the loan is repaid. (83)

mortgage loan: A loan used to buy a house. (83)

N

national debt: Interest owed on money borrowed by the government. (63)

national defense: All goods, services, and groups used to defend a country. (63)

natural resources: All things in nature needed to produce goods and services. (11)

needs: Things people must have to survive. (5)

normal profit: The smallest amount of profit necessary to keep a business operating. (37)

O

organized labor: Workers who have joined together to form labor unions. (39)

P

partnership: A business owned and run by two or more people. (28)

passbook: A booklet used to record transactions in a passbook savings account. (81)

passbook savings account: A type of savings account that uses a passbook to record transactions. (81)

physical: Doing; relating to the body. (11)

picket line: When striking workers parade near a factory or business and carry signs telling why they are striking. (40)

pollute: To make air, land, or water unclean. (11)

poverty: Extreme lack of money. (46)

price: The amount of money a consumer must pay for a good or service. (9)

price war: Competitive lowering of prices between businesses. (24)

private property: Anything a person owns. (31)

producer: A business that makes or provides goods and services. (5)

profit: Money left in a business after all production costs have been paid. (23)

promissory note: A written promise to pay back a loan. (52)

promotion: A better job in the business where someone is employed. (74)

property tax: Tax on private property. (85)

prosperity: A stable or good time financially. (46)

protectionist: One who is against free trade and believes that free trade prevents American goods from being sold. (68)

public goods: Goods or services that can be supplied only by the government. (63)

public utilities: Electric and gas power. (63)

public welfare: Aid from local governments given to people who earn wages below the poverty level. (65)

Q

quota: A limit placed on the amount of a foreign product that can be sold in the United States. (68)

R

rebate: A discount in price. (25)

recession: A gradual slowdown in business activity and consumer spending. (46)

recovery: A time after a recession or depression when businesses start to improve. (46)

regular credit: The kind of credit in which the entire bill must be paid in full at the end of a certain time period, usually thirty days. (78)

rent: Money one person pays for the use of someone else's property. (28)

resources: Things that producers use to make goods and to provide services. (5)

responsibility: A duty or the right thing to do. (37)

retire: To no longer work or hold a job. (48)

revolving credit: The kind of credit in which part of the bill must be paid each month. (78)

riot: A violent disturbance. (40)

S

salary: Money earned for a long period of work, such as a week, month, or year. (12)

sales tax: Taxes paid when goods or services are bought. (85)

scarce: Not enough of a good or service to satisfy all the wants of the people. (15)

serf: One who worked the land in a feudal system. (8)

shortage: When a producer cannot supply enough of a product. (22)

Social Security tax: Tax taken out of people's paychecks and paid by businesses to provide income for the elderly and other persons who are unable to earn an income. (85)

social services: Services to take care of people in need. (63)

socialism: An economic and government system in which the government owns some property and runs some businesses. (88)

sole proprietorship: A business owned by one person. (34)

standard of living: Financial quality of life. (6)

stock: Shares of a company. (18)

stock certificate: A document that shows ownership of stock. (35)

stock exchange: A place where the buying and selling of stock is handled. (82)

stock market: A market in which people buy and sell shares in businesses. (18)

stockbroker: A person paid to help others buy and sell stock. (82)

stockholder: A person who invests money in businesses by buying stocks. (28)

store of value: Something of worth that can be saved or stored for use in the future. (50)

strike: An event in which workers refuse to work until their employers meet certain demands. (40)

supply: The amount of a product that is offered for sale. (20)

surplus: The condition in which there is more of a product than a producer can sell. (22)

T

tariff: A tax placed on an imported product to raise its price. (68)

tax: Money that people and businesses pay to the government. (9)

tax base: The taxable wealth in a community. (85)

technology: The use of scientific knowledge, especially in industry and trade. (43)

tip: Money paid by a customer to a worker for a service. (72)

trial and error: A system by which the best price of a good or service is reached by setting and then lowering a price until consumers buy the good or service. (19)

tying agreement: A seller refuses to sell unless the buyer purchases other products also made by the company. (58)

U

unemployment: Out of a job. (45)

unemployment compensation: Money paid to workers who are let go by their employers. (73)

unemployment insurance: A social program that gives money for a limited time to workers who lose their jobs. (65)

unit pricing: Comparing how much each item costs in a certain amount. (77)

unlimited liability: The owner of a company is responsible for all debts of the company. (34)

W

wage: Money paid per hour of work. (27)

wage and price freeze: A government order to keep prices and wages as they are for a period of time to fight inflation. (48)

wants: Things people would like to have, but do not need to survive. (5)

warranty: A promise made by the maker or the seller of a product that the product is in good working condition. (77)

withhold: To keep back money from a worker's paycheck for taxes. (84)

workers' compensation: Money paid to workers who have been injured or who have become sick because of their job. (73)